10

mich.

HOME GROWN

HOME GROWN

BY

Della T. Lutes

BOSTON
LITTLE, BROWN AND COMPANY
1937

THE ATLANTIC MONTHLY PRESS BOOKS
ARE PUBLISHED BY
LITTLE, BROWN AND COMPANY
IN ASSOCIATION WITH
THE ATLANTIC MONTHLY COMPANY

*To my son, Robert B. Lutes, whose help, both
critical and material, in its writing and preparation
has been invaluable, I dedicate this book*

CONTENTS

HOME GROWN

I

Cousin Saryette Goes into a Decline

My father had come to Southern Michigan when the country was still young and he young with it. This was in the early 1800's. He came — like most of the other early builders of the state, following the pioneers — from York State. He was a carpenter and cabinetmaker and pursued this trade until past middle age, when a cycle of "depression" augmented by the introduction of custom-made furniture took the heart out of his business — but not out of him. He finally, being then a widower, met and married my mother, who was twenty years younger than he, and bought our small farm south of Jackson.

Others of the Thompson clan had followed Uncle 'Lijer from York State from time to time until there were Thompsons by name and Thompson "in-laws" scattered over several townships of Southern Michigan. They were of a gregarious disposition, they loved, admired, and respected Uncle 'Lijer, and my mother was a good cook. We consequently saw quite a lot of them at our house. Occasionally we went to visit them.

Cousin Saryette was the elder of Uncle Frank's and Aunt Catherine's two daughters. The other, 'Melia, was about my own age, which was around eight at the time of this story, and, if I may say so without appearing to hold rancor over a period of more years than it would be wise to name, the stingiest young one I ever knew.

It was upon one such visit to Uncle Frank's that I became bitterly aware of 'Melia's propensity for thrift. No sooner had we got our things off than she took me — a willing and eager follower — to her bedroom to see her toys: a doll — *two* dolls, counting the one made of muslin with painted cheeks and button eyes; a little set of dishes — *real* dishes made of tin; a tiny bureau for the dolls' clothes, and — a cigar box *chock full of candy hearts!* They were the kind that had printed on them words like "Sweetheart!" "When may I see you?" "Would you kiss me?" and similar thrilling — if little understood — inscriptions.

The dolls Amelia would let me hold, but for this privilege I was coldly ungrateful. The kitten that purred around our feet was infinitely more desirable. The tin dishes she let me remove from their cardboard container, even suggesting further use for them in connection with outside water and sand. *But the candy hearts she would not let me touch!*

It was not that they were sweetmeats, for my father almost always brought a few sticks — cinnamon, horehound, pep'mint, or m'lasses — from town, but that they were rare. I longed to finger them, to lay them out in rows, to study them and ponder. I coveted them. Just *one* to clutch in my perspiring hand would have given me indescribable joy, but no. The box was closed, the thin sweetish-smelling cover faintly reminiscent of tobacco was fastened, and the treasure laid away.

When, on a later Sunday, Aunt Hanner and Aunt Sophrony, visiting at our house, told about Cousin Saryette's decline, I felt sorry for her, and wondered why God, in that infinite wisdom which the preacher so volubly bespoke, had not seen fit to lay Amelia low instead.

Aunts Hanner and Sophrony, my father's two sisters, somewhat younger than he, lived in the little village of Millbrook a few miles to our south and west. It was early October and they had driven over themselves on Saturday. Aunt Hanner was a valiant woman, forthright and courageous, who could harness and drive her own horse as well as any man. It took them nearly all day to come, because the roads were very dusty and the horse, my father said, so fat he 'd lather if he switched his tail.

The ostensible object of this visit, if it needed one, was to get a bag of apples and a jug of cider from 'Lijer's store, but the news with which they were bursting had to do with Cousin Saryette.

Now Aunt Hanner and Aunt Sophrony were both widows, but of what you might call two different schools. Aunt Sophrony — the younger, edging sixty on the off side, just under fat, placid, and bordering a little to the south of sentiment — still mourned her husband, who was a victim of the Civil War. Her handkerchiefs had a black border and she drew forth a little green bottle of smelling salts when she spoke of him.

Aunt Hanner — a year or so older and so between her sister Sophrony and her brother 'Lijer, tall and bony, angular, outspoken, and capable — had also had a husband, but the less said about him, apparently, the better. Long before she packed up her rather sumptuous belongings, along with the humbler relics of her sister's wedded life, the Louisiana Lottery and Aunt Hanner's husband had been in some way inextricably confused and the former had in a mysterious and seldom-alluded-to manner been responsible for the demise of the latter. He had left her plenty of money, which interfered in no way with whatever scruples Aunt Hanner may have had regarding its source, and she and Aunt Sophrony lived in a state of comfort and content in their village home.

They were both delightful and interesting women and were always welcome visitors at our house. Especially from a small child's point of view, as they never came empty-handed. Not only had both capacious pockets hidden in the gathers of their voluminous skirts, but they always brought a carpet bag, gayly red and green, which they took, plump and bulging, from the back of the buggy when they arrived, and which was similarly stuffed and stowed when they went.

Cookies, they brought — Aunt Sophrony's cookies, dif-

fering from my mother's in that they were fat where my
mother's were thin, and specked with caraway. Caraway
cookies and gingerbread men — for me. No wonder I
loved to see them come.

Clean, pretty lace caps they also took from the carpet
bag for their graying heads, and long white aprons full-
gathered to a belt that fastened in the back with huge
bows and flowing ties. Aunt Sophrony's had knitted
lace at the bottom, but Aunt Hanner's ended severely
with a hem.

Their knitting and some further gifts also came from
the generous capacity of the bag — socks from Aunt
Sophrony, who was the needlewoman, a packet of seeds
or a bunch of rare herbs from Aunt Hanner's garden.

So here they were, gifts distributed, caps in place,
aprons tied and smoothed, ready to talk, to help my
mother with the meal, to divulge from their store of
neighborly gossip that most pertinent to the occasion.

My father, having seen to the care of their horse,
hastened to the kitchen, where was the scene of immediate activity, since it was nearing supper time. Neither
my father nor my mother had heard about Cousin Saryette.
News did not travel rapidly in that day unless it was
of sufficient importance to warrant a special message.
Whatever it was, Aunt Hanner was clearly put out with
Saryette — and still more so with Aunt Catherine and
Uncle Frank.

"Lettin' a girl her age go to bed and get sick all because a good-for-nothin' skunk like Jerry Oliver up and jilts her! Why don't they make her get up and go to work?"

"Did she go to bed and get sick or get sick and go to bed?" my mother, reasonably enough, wanted to know.

"She come home," stated Aunt Hanner with asperity, "straight from the dance and went to bed. Naturally, she got sick. You can't stay in bed and *not* get sick."

" 'Specially," put in Aunt Sophrony from my mother's rocking chair, where already her knitting needles clicked rhythmically, "if folks begin to dose you with all kinds of stuff."

"Wha 'd he *do* to her?" persisted my mother, halting operations at the stove to make shocked inquiry.

"*Do!* He jilted her. Took her to a bow'ry dance over t' the lake and then took another girl home — town girl named Jess Worden — visitin' Al Brown's folks. Never even *looked* at Saryette after the first dance."

"Well," said my mother spiritedly, turning back to her oven, "why did n't she give him the mitten? Just go ahead and dance, show him a thing or two?"

"Her heart was broke," murmured Aunt Sophrony sympathetically. "She *could n't*."

"Heart fiddlesticks!" sniffed Aunt Hanner. "Girl seventeen! Had n't ought to know she 's *got* a heart. Ought to be in school. What 's she out of school *for?*"

"She *was* going to school this fall," amended Aunt Sophrony gently, "if she had n't been took sick."

"What 's the matter with her?" My mother was putting supper on the table — a pan of beans, hot johnny-cake. "How 's she act?"

Aunt Sophrony gently rocked and knitted. Aunt Hanner was standing around. My father was washing up.

Aunt Hanner snorted. She had a long face and a straight nose, and when she snorted she made me think of a horse. Not *her* horse, for Aunt Hanner was lean and bony, but *a* horse.

"*Act!* She acts like a fool. Won't talk. Won't eat. Now she 's got a cough. They think she 's goin' into gallopin' consumption."

My father made a dreadful noise sputtering the water in the basin. He scrubbed the top of his bald head and wiped it on the roller towel.

"My goodness!" exclaimed my mother, bringing a dish of applesauce and a spice cake from the butt'ry. "Can't they do *anything* with her? Is she really *sick?*"

"She *was n't* sick. But she 's gettin' sick — "

"You seen her?" They were drawing their chairs to the table. My father had n't said a word.

"No," Aunt Hanner said, helping herself to the beans and passing them to Aunt Sophrony. "We ain't. We been so busy — the crab-apple tree was just *loaded* this year and we been makin' jelly, and it 's quite a ways over there. We aim to go over in a week or two. But we saw *him*. Before he jilted her, that is. They's to our house to dinner one Sunday this summer, Frank and Catherine and the girls, and they fetched him. Him and Saryette came alone in his buggy. I didn't think much of him — "

"He's handsome," Aunt Sophrony offered wistfully, as she buttered a piece of johnnycake. Aunt Hanner sniffed again and my father choked on a bean or something. They were an awful lot alike — my father and Aunt Hanner. Chips off the same block, my mother said.

"Handsome!" Aunt Hanner hastily swallowed tea a mite too hot, and all but strangled. "Shif'less do-nothin'. If I'd a been Frank I'd a showed him the door long ago."

"If *I'd* a been Frank," — my father poised a piece of the pork baked with the beans on his fork, and eyed his sister balefully, — "I'd a took down that girl's drawers and licked her till she couldn't set down. Lolly-gaggin' around in *bed*. Consumption, *huh!*" He finally consigned Saryette to the devil and the meat to his mouth, and proceeded with his meal. His womenfolks proceeded with theirs. They were accustomed to his outbursts.

"What they doin' to her?" My mother, pouring tea, passing cream and sugar, mustard pickles, citron preserves, looking after the wants of her guests, pursued the subject. It seemed to fascinate her.

"They couldn't do nothin' for a spell — she wouldn't

let 'em. Now they 're dosin' her on Peruny and some kind of herb tea and pills — I don't know what all."

"Who told you about her?"

"Adelaide. She and Big Jim was over." Adelaide and Big Jim lived not far from the aunts, at the farther side of Millbrook.

My father barked. *"Peruny!"* he growled. "Dollar a bottle!"

"When Cindy Baines died," offered Aunt Sophrony mildly, "and they cleaned the house, they found a *wagon-load* of Peruny bottles in the cellar."

"Yes," sniffed Aunt Hanner scornfully, "and where 'd she die? In the insane asylum. I 'm goin' over to see that girl — "

"You better hold yer tongue," my father advised her shortly. "If you 're goin' to see anybody you better see Frank, and crack his head — tarnation old fool! Prob'ly talks *religion* to her."

My father held Uncle Frank in some contempt, although he liked him. He said Uncle Frank wore a preacher's coat and a jockey's breeches underneath, and he could n't abide it. He said if Uncle Frank 'd shed the coat and wear the breeches he 'd be quite a man.

"If she 's got to die," put in Aunt Sophrony gently, adding a second heaping spoonful of sugar to her tea, "he *ought* to talk religion to her."

My father shoved his chair violently away from the table, and Aunt Hanner poohed and huh'd. They all got up and did the dishes — except my father. He lit a lantern. "Come on, dawtie," he called. "Got to do chores."

We kept hearing about Saryette. Adelaide wrote a letter and said we ought to go to see her. She said folks said Saryette might never live till the snow flew. My father said he'd be dratted if he'd go. He said the room would stink, because Adelaide said they didn't dare let in a breath of air. My mother said he ought to be ashamed of himself, but he wasn't.

We did go to see Saryette, though, but not till after the snow flew. Aunt Hanner wrote and said all the relations had been to see her but us, and Aunt Cathy felt it. My father held out as long as he could, but my mother finally overruled him, and one Sunday in December he hitched up to the pung early in the morning and put in a nice piece of fresh pork and some apples, and my mother put in a lot of jelly and things, and we went.

In case you don't know what a pung is, or was, it was a single bobsled used by the farmer for all manner of utilitarian purposes, and also as a social vehicle when the two-bob sleigh was too large and the cutter too light. And although the automobile has, with smug assurance and haughty arrogance, shouldered all of these as well as other once highly regarded means of conveyance off the road, there are still times when a square-toed, flat-bottomed pung would come in handy. For in spite of all the clamor regarding speed, line, comfort, and convenience, the automobile is still more or less of a fair-weather friend. It presupposes good clear roads and few obstacles. It has Gargantuan strength of which it loudly boasts, but is helpless in the face of storm. Any good roistering, blustering, swaggering bully of a blizzard can make it cower, quail, and quit; while the good old pung, with its slow-moving but trusty motive power ahead, wobbled over drifts, slid over ruts, ploughed through depths, and careened wildly around curves, but got there just the same.

It did, occasionally, tip over. But tipping over in a pung, or even in a sleigh or cutter, was as nothing to tipping over in an automobile. For one thing, you tipped over slowly. The pace at which you moved would never fling you forty feet ahead into tree or post. You had time to prepare for the final catastrophe.

For another thing, you had not far to fall. You were, especially in the pung, pretty much on a level with — or below — any drift you might fall into. You may have been thrust head first into a feathery heap, but you wore a fascinator or a nubia over your hat (if you wore a hat), and a knitted scarf around your neck which kept that portion of your body from harm. Your arm, out-flung, might burrow deep into crystal depths, but you wore mittens and wristlets as a protection to the upper limbs, and long drawers, wool or fleece-lined stockings, high buttoned or laced shoes, and ar'tics, to protect the lower.   So what price a dip or two into the snow as against the surety with which you finally proceeded?

We went, then, to see Saryette in the pung, its odoriferous bottom covered with clean straw and a horse blanket, our legs wrapped in the flannel-lined buffalo robe.

Others were before us — a double cutter with high dashboard and elegant wolf robe.

"Jim's folks," my father laconically remarked as he got stiffly out and we followed him.

Big Jim and Adelaide, it was — and their little girl, Cory.   There were four boys in their family, all older than Cory, but they did not come.

As soon as greetings were over and our wraps removed we were taken to the spare bedroom off the front room, where Saryette lay. Except my father. It took him a long time to look after the horse.

Adelaide, who had, apparently, preceded us by but a few minutes, was in Saryette's room with Cory and Amelia, and as the room was small they came out to make way for us. Not Big Jim. He was out helping Uncle Frank and my father with the horses. Adelaide greeted us tearfully outside the door.

"You go in," she said in a hushed and watery tone. "It's awful!" Cory turned and came back with me. Amelia stayed, smugly watchful.

The whole room was hardly larger than the bed — itself a monstrous affair of pudgy posts, ruffled petticoat, and billowing feather bed.   There was but one small window in it, and that with a thick green shade half drawn, so one could see but little more than a slight depression in the huge bed, a depression outlined under the patchwork quilt and on the pillow by a shadowed halo which shortly became hair wound about a thin, white face.

So *that* was Saryette!   I had seen her at the County Fair, elegantly uncomfortable in new shoes a size too small, and primly disregardful of younger fry.   But Saryette deposed from haughty young ladyhood to potential death was an awesome and a curious sight.

My mother sat down in the chair close beside the bed and took Saryette's hand, wanly extended.   Amelia, belonging, important, lingered by the door.

"How you feelin', Saryette?"   My mother's voice was suddenly attuned to the shadows of the room — the hushed, dead atmosphere of the place.

"Pretty poorly, thank you, Aunt 'Miry.   I cough terrible now."

She gave us a fair sample.   The bed heaved with her convulsive gasps.   We shuddered.

"Don't you want some air in here?"   Mother rose and turned to the window.   She looked a little queer.   I thought about what my father had said.   The room did "stink."   Just then Aunt Cathy came in.   Mother's hand was on the window.

"I thought I 'd open the window a speck," she said. "Seems pretty close — "

Aunt Cathy's hand came down heavily upon her arm. "For mercy's sake, no!" she exclaimed, but in that hushed and fearful tone which people too often use within hearing of the sick. "She must n't have air in from *outside*. It 'd *kill* her."

Mother sat down heavily. Saryette was still coughing, but weakly now. Her mother took up a bottle of dark liquid, a spoon. Holding them against the little square of light, she measured a generous quantity into a glass that stood on a small table at the head of Saryette's bed. Then she poured water into the glass from a pitcher and, bending over, lifted Saryette's thin shoulders from the pillow, and Saryette drank. It must have been a nauseous dose, for she shuddered, retched a bit, and fell back upon her pillow, wan and spent.

Mother half rose. "We better not stay," she said, whispering, and still looking oddly green and queer. "Maybe she wants to sleep."

"Oh, no," Aunt Cathy protested, "you set. She don't want to sleep. If she sleeps now she won't sleep to-night. You 'd like Aunt 'Miry to stay, would n't you, Sar'ette?"

Saryette nodded feebly.

"Pretty soon she has to have her tonic. I 'll measure it out."

Aunt Cathy took up another bottle and a glass. There

seemed to be dozens of them on the small table. "And in about five minutes, 'Miry, you give it to her. I got to go and see about dinner."

Mother waited. Saryette seemed to doze. Then she stirred. "Want your medicine now, Saryette?" Mother leaned gently over the bed.

"No." The wan voice sounded fretful, but held odd potential strength for one so spent. The brown head moved on the pillow, willfully, I thought. "I *hate* it!"

Mother leaned forward. "But your mother said — "

"I don't care. I won't have it!"

Mother settled back in her chair. She still had the odd, half-sick look. She turned to us. "You run along, girls," she said. "I saw some puppies in the kitchen when I came in, and Cousin Saryette wants to sleep."

We ran along. We found the puppies. Dinner came, and we all sat down. It was a long table, well laden. A plate of fried chicken, biscuits, mashed potatoes, and jelly was carried to Saryette.

"Yes," said Aunt Cathy, returning, "she keeps up a purty good appetite now. It's the tonic. If it wasn't for that she wouldn't have had stren'th to last this long."

"Is the tonic Dr. Babcock's prescription?" The queer look still stayed on Mother's face, and her lips had a funny stiffness about them.

"No." Aunt Cathy was short. "Doc Babcock's been pretty mean about Saryette. He said she didn't need no medicine. Said what she needed was spunk." Dr.

Babcock was the community's stay in times of sickness and friend in hours of need. He lived in Millbrook.

My father barely stuck his nose inside the door of Saryette's room.

"Almost knocked me down," he said disgustedly, on the way home. " 'Nough to kill a well person — stay in a room like that."

"Got the window all stuffed with cotton," agreed my mother. "It turned me sick to the stomach. Medicines! Why, they give that girl *six different kinds of medicine!* She could n't get well if she tried. And," she added with emphasis, "what do you think that *tonic* is they 're giving her?"

"Smelt to me," said my father dryly, "like Ol' David H.'s breath."

"Whiskey!" said my mother indignantly. "Besides Peruny and half a dozen other things!"

The sleigh scrunched on the snow. The horses' feet clop-clopped in the soft ruts. Once in a while they threw off a slightly yellowish ball which had accumulated in their shoes. It was growing dusk. A blue light was settling upon the white fields.

"Anyway," my mother broke the padding silence, "I don't believe that girl 's any sicker 'n I am — or would n't be if she 'd get up."

Winter came on. The snow was very deep. We heard nothing from Saryette. She was alive yet, my mother said, or we 'd hear.

Roads were drifted. School was impossible for young children. My father and I both fell victims to colds. My mother made poultices of onions fried in generous quantities of salt-pork fat. Goose grease and skunk's oil alternated. The kitchen stove reeked with concoctions for a cough — honey, butter, and vinegar.

My father's cold ran into lumbago. For this mother devised a mustard plaster of no inconsiderable warmth, as a result of which application my father's groans appreciably increased. When these were followed by sudden silence my mother went to investigate and found the plaster under the bed.

" 'Lije Thompson," she exclaimed, "what in *time* is this plaster doin' *under the bed?*"

Grunting comfortably, my father muttered, "The tarnation thing's so strong I thought it'd draw enough there — and it has."

As the colds disappeared and spring drew near we needed tonics. Sulphur and molasses, of course, was most commonly administered to the defenseless. My father refused to touch it and, as the snow disappeared, concocted his own "bitters." These were made from the roots of rhubarb, yellow dock, dandelion, mandrake, and God knows what else, with the bark of elder and sassafras added. Simmered together for hours, the liquid was then strained off, sweetened with rock candy, and boiled again. This was finally diluted with rye whiskey and bottled for immediate use.

Most of the roots and barks used in these brews were

exceedingly bitter, but the mild flavor of the sassafras, the pure sweetness of the rock candy, and the smooth blend of the liquor tempered the bitterness and made a potion doubtless not unpleasant to an unjaded palate.

What actual and medicinal benefit accrued from the use of these libations is not for a lay commentator to say, but that there was tonic quality in the gathering and drying and preparation, and in the sincerity of faith with which they were consumed, is beyond doubt.

As the roads cleared my mother began to express a hope that they could soon get over to see Saryette. The old women had given her until snow flew, but the snow had come and gone and she was apparently still amongst the living. Occasional letters from Aunt Hanner or Sophrony spoke of her, but in an entirely noncommittal manner.

"Why don't they *say* something?" stormed my mother. "You wouldn't think she'd ever been sick."

"Well," agreed my father, "she prob'ly ain't."

One Sunday Big Jim and Adelaide made us a visit. Before the men came in from the barn, my mother fairly pounced upon Adelaide for news of Saryette.

"My land!" exclaimed Adelaide. "Ain't you heard?" She giggled girlishly, tying a full white apron over her Sunday dress. Adelaide, though the mother of a generous family, would ever be a girl.

"I ain't heard a word," said my mother impatiently. "What happened, for mercy's sake?"

"Saryette got mad," said Adelaide, still laughing. "You know who Hat Webster is?"

My mother shook her head.

"She's the worst old tattletale in three counties — lives in Millbrook, but she knows the news. She went to make over Cathy's black cashmere. Cathy prob'ly thought she's goin' to need it any minnit and better have it ready. Well, Hat was regalin' 'em with all the news, — they was sewin' in the front room there, where Saryette's room is off from, — when all of a sudden Hat says, 'Have you heard about Jerry Oliver's latest performance?' Well, Cathy almost jumped out of her chair. She 'Sh-sh-'d' and motioned, but she could n't shut Hat up. Not without knockin' her down. Hat had her head bent over the machine and was talkin' above it. 'He's jilted that Worden girl now and got him another,' she says. 'Grass widder this time.'

"Well, Cathy got up and tiptoed over to Saryette's door and was pullin' it shut when Saryette spoke up. 'Leave the door open, Ma,' she says, and Cathy said she's like to drop.

" 'Had n't I better close it?' says Cathy, meek 's Moses. 'The machine makes such a noise.' 'No,' says Saryette, firmer 'n ever, 'you need n't.' So Cathy leaves the door open and comes back and sets down to her sewin'. Her face's fairly yellow, though, an' she keeps glancin' first at Hat Webster and then at the door. Hat kep' right on. 'Jed Oliver,' she says, 'had met this grass widder at a dance where he'd took the Worden girl. He danced with the widder,' she said, 'five times hand-runnin', includin' the supper dance, and then did n't he load her into the cutter along with him *and* the Worden girl and take the Worden girl home *first!* This grass widder, — her name's Hanson, — she's set up a shop of some kind over to Hanover, and the next Sunday night he drove over there and took her cutter ridin'. And he ain't been near the Worden girl since.'

"All this time the machine's runnin' like mad, you understand," Adelaide went on, "and Cathy's settin' there lookin' like death, pullin' bastin's out of the black cashmere. And every little while she looks over at Saryette's door as if she expected her to be carried out, feet first.

"Stead of that, what does Saryette do but get up and dress! That very night after Hat Webster'd gone. Cathy told me about it herself. Said Saryette called her in and told her she wanted her clothes. Cathy said she thought what Hat said had gone to her head. But Saryette was bent — she was always pretty stubborn; if she had n't been she could n't have stayed in bed six months — and so Cathy fetched her clothes. Saryette was awful weak, she said, but soon's she got on her feet she seemed to take holt. She put on her clothes and went out and sat down to the supper table. Cathy said she felt exactly as if a ghost was settin' there. And Frank, he just set and bellered, tears a-runnin' down

into his soup. But Frank's soft anyway. And Saryette ain't been back to bed since, exceptin' to sleep
nights."

"Well," said my mother, as a cold blast preceded the
two men, my father and Big Jim, who were coming in
the door, "did she ever *say* anything?"

"Yes," said Adelaide, "she said she was n't goin' to let
no white-livered sap 't did n't know his own mind make
a fool of her. You see, she did n't have to feel ashamed
no longer — alone. There was the Worden girl too."

II

The Tin Dinner Pail

THE tin dinner pail, in the days of my early education, was the pivotal point around which the day revolved — that and the water pail. The latter reposed on a bench near the schoolhouse door with a tin dipper either in it or hanging from a near-by nail. Just above was a shelf for the dinner pails.

Going after water was the one great treat of the day. You went to the nearest neighbor's well, for replenishment of the supply, and by judicious dallying could break the monotony of the morning session to the extent of a quarter of an hour or more. In the afternoon the ritual was repeated, but no country boy or girl would any more have thought of rendering such service during the noon hour than of voluntarily staying in at that time to do sums. They would go to the well, one and all — even the teacher, if she wanted a drink; but to "go after water" at any time except during the school session would have been a silly thing — defrauding oneself of a sacred privilege.

The next most coveted service to the welfare of this

small community was "passing the water." To accomplish this act of mercy the privileged dispenser would fill the quart tin dipper brimming full at the pail and, beginning with the front seat, allow its occupant to drink his fill. The dipper was then passed to the next and this procedure repeated until it was empty. Then it was refilled and its dripping, splashing, slopping way pursued until the entire stock, so to speak, had been watered while Teacher looked complacently on, or proceeded with the routine of lessons, unperturbed by any prophetic qualms concerning zymotic results. If any portion of the last dipperful remained it was slopped back into the pail.

The dinner hour, somewhat less communal in spirit, was nevertheless one of no small social importance, as well as of physical satisfaction mingled with a modicum of speculation.

In the first place, as we had breakfasted at some hour not far from dawn, there was hunger to be allayed, and even though buckwheat cakes, pork sausage, and fried potatoes may have formed the *pièce de résistance* of the meal, a walk of a mile or more in fair weather or foul, and a breach of five or six hours between, could arouse an urgent interest in food.

Then there was, in my own case at least, the possible element of surprise. My mother had no great store on which to draw in making up a lunch for a hungry child, but she did exercise here the same priceless quality that in general set her cooking above that of many of her contemporaries — the element of imagination aided and supported by a sense of the fitness of food to its purpose.

No surprise, however, could have taken the place of the integral source of sustenance, such as the bread and butter that formed the main part of the school lunch. Bread baked in our own kitchen at least three times a week, fresh, moist, and fragrant with the musky odor of wheat not yet too far removed from the flour which held the greater part of its nutriment. Not the salt-rising bread which was my father's favorite (the only kind he considered fit to eat). This my mother said she would not put to the test of imprisonment in a tightly closed tin pail for five or six hours. Salt-rising bread, as made by her and her contemporaries, had a peculiar and not altogether pleasing odor during its process of rising, and my mother, with whom this particular kind was not a favorite, held that something of the odor could be detected even after the baking. My father said maybe it could, and if folks had the sense to appreciate it they'd be glad of it. Mother always made it under protest, — at least she voiced a protest, — but one which neither she nor my father took seriously. My father, so he said, had been *raised* on salt-risin' bread back in York State. It was the kind his mother made, he'd always been used to it, and by jiminy he was going to have it. His own sisters, Aunts Hanner and Sophrony, could not — or would not — verify this. They said they did n't remember what kind of bread their mother had made besides johnny-cake, but prob'ly she did make salt-risin'. And any-way, 'Lije was the spoiled brother in a family of girls, and all were fond of their vittles. He had had only to express a preference and they had, to a woman, his mother most of all, tumbled over each other to satisfy him. *They* would n't humor him so, they said, but even I, as a small child when we went to visit them in the little town of Millbrook, noticed that if they knew we were coming, there was always at least one of my father's favorite dishes on the table.

Of course the bread that went into my dinner pail was buttered from the contents of a stone churn, the dasher of which I sometimes unwillingly manipulated. And while the butter with which I can still dress my salt-risin' bread, when in Michigan, is good, — even sometimes home-churned, — I cannot be persuaded that it has *q-u-i-t-e* the sapient flavor, the *exactly* correct proportion of salt, *j-u-s-t* the right amount of "work-ing" to free it from the milk, that had that other of my youth. For one thing, there are newfangled ways of making it, those "improved methods" of questionable value. The milk, in the first place, is not allowed to "lobber." We used to let the milk "lobber" on the cellar shelves and then skim off the thick, rich yellow cream with a tin skimmer. Nowadays they separate it while still sweet — an unnatural process as ever was, disuniting cream from milk not yet brought to that state of ripeness where it is ready to part with its better half. A process which, besides going plumb against nature, affords no buttermilk.

Now buttermilk, as emanating from a stone churn after the butter has been not too parsimoniously ladled out, properly salted and cold, is as appetizing, healthful, and delicious a beverage as ever appeased a thirsty throat. Its disappearance from the list of natural beverages is a distinct loss to man, a loss equal in epicurean value to that of "riz" buckwheat cakes from the breakfast menu. No chemical laboratory, however superior in sanitary measure, can compensate the true buttermilk lover for the authentic article. However, since a modern public has nothing more than a name by which to judge, perhaps it is as well to condone the deception. To *know* what good buttermilk is like and then not be able to get it would be but one more cruelty perpetrated upon an already defeated appetite.

My father maintained that a woman's housewifely reputation depended upon her skill in butter making. He said let him taste the butter a woman made and he could tell you what was on her cellar shelves and what kind of friedcakes she made. He said the only time in the world he had any sympathy for Old Covell was when he thought of the kind of butter Miz' Covell prob'ly made. No, he'd never tasted it and he never wanted to. You'd know by looking at her.

(The Covells were that family of shiftless neighbors on our east, a thriftless crew composed of an improvident father, a slatternly mother, and four consequently neglected children — all girls; always borrowing, never returning, a perennial trial to my mother, anathema to my father.)

Butter, my father maintained, didn't want so much to *taste* of "medder" grass and grain as it wanted to make you *think* of such things when you ate it. He would have had small patience with the modern fad of serving butter unsalted, and if any such had been served him at any of the taverns where he happened to stop, he would have had it out with the landlord. He would have given him a "schoolin'" for foisting a tasteless grease upon him in the place of butter. It took salt, he said, to bring out that exact nicety of flavor which sets good cow butter forever apart from every and any other similar enriching food devised by man's efforts to improve on nature.

Then, too, my mother knew how to spread butter on bread. This may sound like a performance too simple of execution to be worthy of note or comment, but the cultured palate knows that the affinity of butter for bread is one of delicate distinction. Butter should not be spread on bread after the manner of greasing the axle of a wagon, nor yet with the penurious hand of a pinchpenny. One of the worst things my father could say of a woman was that she put butter into her mashed potatoes with a teaspoon. There is a *mean* to butter spreading like that of the dispensation of salt in cookery — too little will spoil the meat, too much will spoil the broth. There is more to the *flavor* of butter than to the odor, for the smell of too much butter on the bread can be offensive, as those of you who have ever taught country school and suffered from the proximity of buttered cheeks can testify.

Especially in the matter of buttering toast do women err. Butter *will* melt, of course, if the toast is hot enough, and it will spread toward distant shores if left to follow a natural course, but in such case one portion of the toast becomes sodden with grease while the edges remain barren and dry.

Whether toasted or untoasted, bread should be *spread* with butter, neither saturated nor stinted. And this is as true of making sandwiches as in any other use, although one must admit that the danger from any immoderate supply of butter on the commercial sandwich is but slight.

Butter, to be properly spread, should be brought to just the right consistency for smooth manipulation with a thin-edged knife. To take it from the refrigerator or cold room, cut off hunks, and then try to bend these to the bread is only to crumble the latter and lose the value of the first. In such instance you must eat now a piece of bread unbuttered and again a piece of butter unbreaded. Butter should be soft enough to spread on the bread, but not soft enough to run into it.

When I was a child, sandwiches had not arrived at that place in dietary use which to-day is second only to the salad. Nor had we peanut butter — a matter of some regret — or any of the multitudinous "spreads" of to-day — less deplored. But when, after an early breakfast, my mother found a thin slice of fried ham left over, and slipped it between two fragrant slices of moist, evenly buttered bread, she was providing a delightful salty surprise for the dinner pail. On the other hand, when Miz' Covell would outrage more than the eye by sticking a slab of cold fried salt pork between two slices of unbuttered bread, she was but prophetically portraying the abuse to which good bread has since been put. Salt pork is all right in its place, but it is not recommended as sandwich timber, and neither are many other things so victimized. The sandwich is indeed a versatile comestible, but sins unnumbered have been and are daily being committed in its name.

The opening of the dinner pails in the country school, upon the very instant of dismissal, was, as has been intimated, a matter of conjecture and speculation. Not so much as to what *you* had in your pail, the packing of which you may have supervised, but as to what someone else had. Barter and trade ran high at the dinner hour, and those children whose mothers held the highest reputation in the culinary art, unless strengthened by unhappy experience as well as by parental injunction ("Now, *don't* let those Covell young ones tease your dinner away from you. You *know* you can't eat theirs!"), were likely to go home at night in a state of hungry bitterness. The Covells were the worst offenders in wheedling tidbits from the less aggressive children, a practice from which I frequently suffered. When, after repeated raids upon the cooky jar before I could even stop to get my wraps off, investigation proved that I had had virtually nothing to eat since breakfast because I could not eat what the Covells offered, my father threatened a visit to the teacher, the Covells, and perhaps the whole school board. Then my mother took to putting in two or three extra slices of cake or a couple of cookies, in order to insure my own. "All danged foolishness," declared my father. "More you give 'em, more they'll take. Make Old Covell feed 'em. Got just as much to do with as I have."

Released odors, as the tin tops were pried out of the pails, often gave out advance information regarding contents. That of sour pickles predominated, injudiciously mixed with the aroma of chocolate cake or friedcakes. My own mother did not favor me with the

sour pickle. Not because of any nutritional prejudices
on her part, but simply because pickles soaked the pie
or cake or, what was a still greater offense, the bread and
butter. Since I was past seven years of age before I
ever set foot inside a schoolhouse, a pickle more or less
on top of the salt-pork-and-milk-gravy diet which formed
the bulk of our subsistence would not, in all probability,
have seriously affected my digestion. But that I should
have to eat a piece of *her* bread soaked by a pickle was
unthinkable; and so my fresh, unpolluted bread, my
red-brown spice cake richly imbedded with raisins, were
fair plunder for the cunning speculator.

Often, too, there would be an addition to the well-
packed pail — perhaps a small glass of jelly, with one of
Grandmother's old silver spoons to eat it with. ("Now
you be careful of that spoon. That belonged to your
Grandmother Bogardus. Her mother brought it all the
way from Holland, where they went when they run
away from France.") Or a little jar of baked beans with
another of piccalilli or chili sauce. A few years later,
but while I was still carrying a tin dinner pail to school,
my father began raising celery, and to this day I have
never found anything so appetizing, tasty, and satisfying as the crisp, sweet hearts of celery that accompanied my bread and butter for lunch.

My father blanched his celery in a primitive way with
boards and dirt, but later, when freezing weather came,
he buried it in an earth pocket and covered it with

straw as he did other vegetables. When it was taken out later in the winter it was so crisp that it would break at the touch, not entirely white, but creamy in color and nutty in flavor.

The standard dinner pail of my early school days contained two or three slices of bread of more than generous thickness, maybe a hunk of some kind of cold meat, a hard-boiled egg, a piece of pie, a doughnut, and — for most — the inevitable pickle. If there was room for an apple it went in. Otherwise it went into a coat pocket. I seldom found a friedcake in my pail, not, again, because a friedcake was considered at all objectionable for an eight- or ten-year-old youngster, but because I had had one with my mug of milk in the morning, and one was enough. A slice of spice cake, applesauce cake, or a molasses drop cooky was thought better. They were also more favored by the Covells.

The oldest of the Covell girls was about fourteen. Two younger ones went to school. They were also half-starved, not even half-dressed, and were a constant object of anxiety to the neighbors, not in themselves, but because they were the visible evidence of their parents' incompetence.

"Old coot," declared my father irascibly of the sire, in one particular instance. "Ought to be rode on a rail. Lettin' girls go to school so hungry they got to steal an' beg, and barefoot! Last of October! Ain't they got no *shoes?*" The ferocity of his demand would appear to place the blame on my mother, at whom he glared.

"No," said my mother worriedly, "they ain't. Miz' Covell told me they have n't got a shoe amongst 'em. It 's a shame. That oldest girl 's smart — "

"Huh!" grunted my father. "The old coot think they can go to school barefoot all winter? Freezin' weather any day now."

"I 'm afraid," admitted my mother anxiously, " 't he don't care whether they go to school or not. Miz' Covell told me they could n't go after it 's too cold to go barefoot."

My father shoved his chair back from the table.

"Ought to be a law," he fumed. "Somebody 'd ought to do something."

My mother's eyes followed him solicitously. When my father gave himself of the opinion that something ought to be done, he usually set about doing it, but such activity occurred only after his sense of injustice or unfairness had been brought to the boiling point. In general he was all for minding his own business and encouraging others to do the same. He was, however, a forthright man and did his duty as he saw it without undue consideration of consequences.

What he did about it took place a few weeks later. Sure enough, the ground had frozen, snow had fallen, and winter was close upon us even though Indian summer might follow. The Covells stayed home from school. So, on the bad days, did I. There would be weeks to come when my own education, such as it was, would be pursued under my mother's tutelage. It consisted of a perusal of whatever old books were to be found at our and other houses, as well as of the almanac, and intimate contact with the well-stored minds of my father and mother. My father was an excellent penman of the Spencerian school and supervised my use of the pencil and pen. He also undertook to instill into my mind some of the principles of mathematics under what he called "the Rule of Three," a process which I was never able to master, to his impatient distress.

The fact, therefore, that the Covell girls would be deprived of a few months' attendance at the "deestrick" school was not of sufficient importance to arouse family indignation to the extent which prevailed. Their feet would suffer almost as much from exposure to the bare floors of their house as to the ground outside, and this was part of the grievance. It was the standard of their living that pricked. Old Covell had a good farm, but he was, as my father said, too "tarnation lazy" to farm it. He would plant potatoes in the spring and then neglect to cultivate them. Most of the work accomplished was done by his wife and children. This particular year he had raised a number of hogs and done a pretty good job at fattening them. In fact he had turned them into the cornfield and let them fatten themselves. Early in November he butchered five, and one day took all but one to town. This was left hanging, to be cut up and salted for their own use.

"Well," said my father comfortably, having watched Old Covell with his load of hogs go past, "now the children 'll have some shoes anyway."

But the children were not to have their shoes, at least from that immediate source. Miz' Covell came over to our house that afternoon to borrow some molasses, and told why.

"He said," she narrated dully, " 't if he did n't come home by night I 'd know he 'd gone up Nawth."

"Gone up Nawth?" repeated my father, instantly irritated and suspicious. "What 'd he go up Nawth for?"

"Why, huntin'," she replied vacuously. "He said he c'd make more goin' up Nawth for deer than he could on what the hogs 'd fetch."

"Mean to set there and tell me," roared my father, " 't that old coot 's took the money from them hogs and gone *huntin'* with it?"

Miz' Covell guessed he had. That was what he had said — if he did n't get home by night — said he might be gone a week. Said the weather 'd likely hold, and if it did n't she could prob'ly get my father to cut up the hog.

My father was never a profane man, but he had a certain supply of expletives that seemed to give him

ease in moments of great trial. Now, however, these
failing him, and stronger phrases being foreign to his
tongue, silence was the only alternative. He grabbed
up his old felt hat and stalked from the house, fairly
exuding fumes of wrath. When he returned, smelling
of the soothing companionship of horses and of the
frostbitten air of a November day, Miz' Covell was
still there. She seemed loth to leave the comfort and
warmth of our kitchen.

My father drew up a chair and sat down before her.
"I tell you what, Miz' Covell," he said decisively, "you
listen to me. Of course I 'd be glad to help you cut
up that hog, but I got an awful busy day to-morrow —
fact is, I got to go to Jackson. And that hog 's goin' to
spoil sure 's shootin'. There 's a thaw in sight and the
almanac says mild spell of weather. Now I 'll tell you
what you do. The girls need shoes, don't they?"

"Why, yes," she admitted, wondering, "they ain't
got none. I ain't neither." She stuck out a bunioned
foot clad in the shreds of a pair of old felt slippers.
"We ain't none of us got shoes — 'cept Pa. He got
hisself some last time he went to town."

My father hitched his chair impatiently, but managed
to maintain an urbane and beneficent air. "Well," he
said ingratiatingly, "I figger it this way. It 'd be too bad
if the hog should spoil with this thaw comin' on, and
seein' as I 'm goin' to be so busy the next few days,
it may. Now I 'll take the hog to town to-morrow and

sell it for you — " Miz' Covell's expressionless eyes
lit with doubt and fear, but my father quickly proceeded. "I 'll sell the hog for you, and you go along, you
and the girls, and get you some shoes, and that 'll pay
for 'em. You get some shoes for all of you — and some
dresses too," he added magnanimously. "It 's *your*
hog, you know — "

"We would n't have a thing to eat," she interrupted
him worriedly. "That 's our pork for winter — "

"Shaw!" exclaimed my father largely. "Covell 's got
more hogs. I seen 'em to-day. Good condition, too.
I 'll let you have some pork when I butcher and you
c'n pay me back later. Now — " he sprang up nimbly,
shoved back his chair, and brought the woman to her
feet by the sheer exuberance of his own act — "you go
home 'nd get the children all cleaned up. Wash their
feet good — "

"They ain't got no shoes to wear to town — "

"They got stockin's, ain't they?"

"Well, I — "

" 'Miry — " he turned impetuously to my mother,
"you fish out some stockin's for Miz' Covell and the
girls. They 're goin' to town with me to-morrow —
you and Delly c'n go along. I 'll set you down to the
shoe store and you can pick out the shoes. Then I 'll
sell the hog and come back and pay for 'em."

Miz' Covell had but little will of her own at any time
and the immediate influence sufficed to move her. In

the morning, therefore, when we drove up in the democrat wagon with plenty of buffalo robes and old quilts with which to cover the shoeless feet, she and her brood were ready. The light of adventure sparkled in five pairs of eyes, usually hopeless and dull. Late afternoon saw us returning with every present Covell shod and shivering with joy. My father thumped the reins on the horses' backs, called them a pair of old coots, and wanted to know why in tunket they couldn't move a little faster. He hummed under his breath and glanced back at the smirking Covells with the air of a benevolent god. My mother was silent. She of all the load of satisfied humanity wondered what would happen when Old Covell got home. Later, she expressed her concern to my father after he had unloaded the Covells with their several precious packages at their own door, but he remarked loftily, "Shaw! Who cares? He can't *do* anything about it — they got the shoes, ain't they? And, besides, mebbe it would of spoilt. The almanac *did* say 'mild.'"

What Old Covell did about it, as near as we ever learned, was to fume. Amarita, the oldest girl, told us afterward that her pa blew her ma up something awful for letting that meddlin' old Thompson next door stick his fingers in *his* business. She said her pa said he guessed he knew enough to buy his childern shoes when they needed 'em, and he said if my pa 'd minded his business and left things alone till *he* got home, *he'd* of got 'em shoes a lot better 'n what they did get. He said he was goin' right plumb over to Thompson's and tell that ole cuss what he thought. But, she said, her ma did n't care. Her ma said, anyway, they got the shoes. And the only thing Ol' Covell ever said to my father was that he was much obliged for the trouble he took gettin' red of the hawg 'fore it thawed, and 't if he 'd a got a deer he 'd a give him some.

The affluence in wearing apparel, however, marked no special conversion on the part of the young Covells. So far as the dinner pail was concerned they continued to wheedle at least a part of the contents of mine every day.

"Your mother 's an awful good cook, ain't she?" commented Amarita one day, munching ravenously on my one choice cake. The proof, it would seem, was in the eating, and I had no other reply.

"Ma says she is," continued my unsought beneficiary. "She says she has to be because your pa 'd raise Cain if she did n't cook things good. Ma says your pa 'd ruther eat 'n go fishin'."

I knew that my father liked to eat, and that he also liked to go fishing. Toward which of these two pastimes his warmer preference led I remained in ignorance. I had also seen him using a cane at such times as he suffered from a crick in the back, but I did not remember ever to have seen him use it in any such manner as indicated. I therefore took the matter to my mother.

"Ma," I said, "would Pa raise his cane if you did n't cook things good?"

"What do you mean?" My mother lifted surprised and questioning eyes to mine. "Who said anything about raising a cane?"

I told her. "Amarita Covell said that her ma said if you did n't cook things good, Pa 'd raise his cane. And she said Pa 'd rather eat than go fishing."

"Well," said my mother dryly, "he prob'ly would — when he 's hungry. But," she added pointedly, "you want to remember that if your pa wants things cooked good, it 's because he *knows* when they 're good. And he won't eat 'em if they ain't."

"What 'd he do with his cane?"

"That," explained my mother, with some disdain, "was n't what she meant. They say a body 'll raise Cain when they scold and holler and make a terrible fuss. It 's another kind of cane."

"Well," persistently, "would he?"

"Yes," said my mother truthfully and not without pride, "he prob'ly would. And he 'd have a right to," she added defensively. "Cooking 's a woman's job. She 's *got* to cook. It 's laid out that way. So, if she 's got any pride, she 'll want to do it the best she can. That 's the way it ought to be and that 's the way it is."

To find recipes that will give results satisfactorily comparable to those used in my mother's day is not an altogether easy thing. Take the applesauce cake now: In testing various old rules which have been routed out of drawer and file and floury book, I have tried to send a scouting memory back to the cake my mother made, red-brown in color, velvet to the touch, spicily Oriental in odor, richly lickerish in taste. I have tried to evoke my father's nicety of discrimination in flavor, watchful of his salty verdict, hopeful for his praise. He did not care as much for cakes in general as he did for pies and certain rich puddings, — the kind of puddings that, as he said, had something to get your teeth into, — but, since cake was a generally accepted finale to supper, he had his favorites. Applesauce cake was one.

I have also tried to remember the cunning of my mother's hand. One after another rule has been tried, some found wanting, some found good, and finally one that seems a very incarnation of the one that often topped the last meal of the day, often graced my dinner pail, or offered too great a temptation to the tottering morality of the Covell tribe. Here it is: —

Take one cup of good-tasting applesauce and sweeten it with a cup of brown sugar which has been well blended with a half cup of butter. Then mix one teaspoonful of baking soda and one of baking powder with two cups of flour and stir it into the applesauce together with a teaspoonful each of cinnamon, cloves, allspice, and nutmeg. Finally, stir in a cupful of chopped raisins. Pour into a well-buttered oblong bread tin and bake slowly in an oven not too hot.

The molasses drop cookies were made by my Grandmother Bogardus's rule. We usually had them on the table for breakfast, although my father seldom touched them. He preferred his friedcakes. But they went well with a mug of fresh morning's milk, and what were left over were found in the dinner pail at noon. They were a great favorite with the Covells, and although Miz' Covell had begged the recipe, and frequently borrowed the molasses with which to make them, I counted myself lucky when one was left by the time I had finished my bread and butter.

"Take" — most of the old rules began by "taking" something — "take one egg and, after beating it well, mix well with one cup of brown sugar and one cup of soft butter and lard, half each. Mix together one cup of molasses and one of hot water and stir two teaspoonfuls of baking soda into this. Add this to the molasses, sugar, and shortening. Stir in one teaspoonful each of ginger, cinnamon, and salt, with enough flour to thicken it so it will drop from a spoon. Grease a dripping pan and drop the dough onto it in small round cakes. Press a raisin in the middle of each, and bake."

My grandmother lived a long way off, — seventy-five miles, near Detroit, — and I had never visited her but once. Once in a great while she came to see us and always brought these cookies, besides having sent the recipe. My mother kept them in a brown crock with a wide mouth.

The water pail and the dipper have gone the way of the "tin peddler" whose periodic visit through the community cleared the woodshed of rag bags, enhanced the charm of our kitchens with bright new wares, and increased the efficiency of our equipment with new brooms and mop handles.

Judging by the number of rural pupils pouring into the consolidated schools, with a parsimoniously small paper bag or a paper parcel in their hands, it looks as if the dinner pail were going the same way. Where a hot lunch is provided in the school, this is not to be regretted. But, remembering the pleasure it was, after a morning of seeming eternity, to open a pail filled with appetizing, if humble, food, I should regret a modern disregard for the stomach that could accept a sandwich in a paper bag in place of that competent tribute to a natural demand. And if the honorable Parent-Teacher organization is looking around for some worthy pursuit, I suggest that it encourage a reasonable substitute for the dinner pail, with, for those who will acknowledge the need, advice regarding its contents and, possibly, directions for their preparation. A heart of celery with a little packet of salt, and a couple of slices of good bread and butter, are much to be preferred to a lettuce sandwich with the lettuce become flaccid, wilted, damp, and butter-soaked. Peanut butter, different kinds of spread, are all well enough as variants, but good sweet bread and butter with some crisp, well-wrapped green, and a wholesome sweet with fruit as a finish, are infinitely more appetizing, and therefore more nourishing, than an insipid sandwich in a paper bag.

The argument, one hears, for this transient container is the children's own, and based on the premise that it doesn't have to be lugged home. A little firm persuasion on the part of the parent, with coöperative encouragement from the teacher, might tend toward a fuller and more leisurely consumed lunch, with greater receptivity toward the afternoon session, even if such procedure does entail the laborious task of "lugging" home a small lunch box.

The tin dinner pail of my childhood had its faults, but there were agreeable associations connected with it (in spite of the Covells), and it had no small part in the building and establishment of a fairly healthy citizenry.

III

An Old-Fashioned Sunday-Night Supper

THE Larrabees lived two miles or so from where we did, but on another road. They had a big farm, much of it in wheat, oats, and corn, for farmers in those days grew the grain for their own stock and a considerable amount for their own eating as well. They had a large house which sat well back from the road, with two rows of rounded maples marching up to it and shading the drive. These Mr. Larrabee's father had set out when he took the land from the government at a dollar and a quarter an acre. There were also huge barns, wagon sheds, tool houses, corncribs, and an orchard across the road. Beyond the orchard was a little lake where the boys swam and fished. The garden was behind the house.

There were eight children in the Larrabee family — the two oldest, Caroline and Phillip, married and living on their own farms not far away. The rest of the children were laddered two years apart as regularly as if arranged according to chronological scale. They were all older than I except Janey, the youngest, who was

of my own age, and as they went to a different school
from the one I attended there was but little intimacy
between us until I was about ten. Mrs. Larrabee had,
however, frequently invited my mother (and me) to the
Ladies' Aid meetings and the Sewing Circle, and we went
to the same church. Mr. Larrabee bought plants of
my father in the spring, and occasionally hired him to
do a little carpenter work.

Sometimes Janey or one of the other children came
to our house with their father, or I accompanied mine
to the Larrabee place, but the year that Janey and I
were both ten saw what had been a neighborhood acquaintance grow into a real friendship.

One Saturday afternoon in early winter my father
went over to help Mr. Larrabee repair his sheep shed,
and I went along. Janey and I had a great time playing in the haymow and watching the hired man run a
grist of buckwheat through the fanning mill — such a
good time that when dusk came on and my father
called that it was time to go home I hated to go, and
Janey set up a howl for me to stay all night. Now I
had never stayed away from home in my life except
once at my Cousin Adelaide's, and I was not only skeptical
of being allowed, but a little reluctant. To be thrust suddenly into the midst of this big roistering family for
all night was a prospect somewhat overwhelming to a
shy only child.

Mrs. Larrabee, who came to the door, added her plea

to Janey's, and further stipulated that my father and mother should come after me Sunday evening, after the chores were done.

To this my father instantly and vigorously demurred. He said he couldn't come out after dark because he wouldn't want to leave the fires burning. Mrs. Larrabee thought the fires could be safely banked. He said my mother would think that was too late for me — she'd probably scold anyway because he had left me, and, come to think of it, I had better go along home with him.

At this I broke into violent despair and begged to stay, supported by Janey's tears. Well, then, I might stay, but he would come for me right after dinner, maybe before. At this moment Mrs. Larrabee, apparently overcome with belated hospitality, remembered that she had a fresh gingerbread just out of the oven. Would he come in for a moment so that she could send some of it to my mother?

He could hardly refuse such a request — and perhaps he did not want to, warm gingerbread being a weakness with him.

We went in. Mrs. Larrabee's kitchen was a beautiful room with a shelf of flowers in the middle of a sunny window, and it was so full of the spicy aroma of molasses and ginger as to invoke a spontaneous flow of eager juices.

There, on an oilcloth-covered table, was the gingerbread — *two* gingerbreads, one of which Mrs. Larrabee proceeded to wrap in an immaculate towel while my father and I stood near the door waiting. Tildy, the hired girl, was taking a pan of cookies from the oven.

"I know this gingerbread won't be as good as Miz' Thompson makes," Mrs. Larrabee said depreciatingly, putting a second towel around it. "I 've had some of hers and it can't be beat; but anyway this is fresh. I made it myself — Tildy 's bakin' pies and cookies. Tildy, you get a plate and put some of those cookies on it. And get a pitcher of cider. Mr. Thompson, you set up here and have a cooky and some cider."

My father mumbled a feeble objection, but Mrs. Larrabee had him in a chair — with me in another — before his hesitancy could take lingual form.

"This is new cider," said Mrs. Larrabee, busily filling glasses. "We just got it home this week." She set cookies before us, and then, as a climax, brought a huge wedge of fresh mince pie and a generous chunk of yellow cheese and put these before my father.

"I 'm not giving Delly any," she explained kindly, "because I don't want to spoil her supper."

"No danger spoiling *my* supper, I s'pose," chuckled my father, neatly fitting a slice of cheese to a piece of the pie with his knife. "Not with mince pie, anyhow."

Mr. Larrabee came in and they exchanged salty quips in country fashion — a waggery which I was in no humor to appreciate, for as yet no decision had been reached as to my immediate future. My father's weakness where good food was concerned, however, seemed to have traveled beyond the confines of the family circle; and when, his palate flattered, his heart warmed with neighborliness, he rose to go, Mrs. Larrabee held me within a possessive arm and said, "Now you and Miz' Thompson come over after Delly to-morrow night, won't you? The family 'll all be home and we 're going to have a reg'lar Sunday-night supper. We want you both to come."

Under the circumstances, with a still-warm gingerbread in his hands and his stomach milling the grist of hospitality, what could the poor man do?

To an only child brought up with grown relatives, — mostly nieces, nephews, and cousins in varying degree, of my father's, — the Larrabee household, with its good wholesome noise and constantly flowing activity, was a never-ending source of delight.

For one thing, they were all what was called "musical." Elizabeth, twenty and through with school, "took voice" and went twice a week to Spring Arbor Academy for lessons; Charlie, the oldest son at home, and twenty-two, sharing the farm work with his father, played the fiddle — by ear; and young Henry could wangle a tune out of a mouth organ that would set even the preacher's solemn foot to beating time.

And sing! Why, they all — including the father, the mother, and even the hired man — sang as naturally and almost as tunefully as the song sparrows that nested, summers, in the fields across the road. Even Tildy lifted up a rhythmic if resonant voice when the family joined in melodious praise to the Lord after morning prayers on the Sabbath. Hester, eighteen, had a really lovely voice, and little Janey caroled like a thrush. So the humming activity that constantly emanated from the Larrabee farmhouse had the same pleasant euphony as a hive of bees or a cote of birds.

My father was not of a gregarious nature, nor inclined to leave his own fireside for any social occasion whatever, much less one that took him out at night with encroachment upon his early bedtime hour. This time, however, he had been outgeneraled, and so on Sunday night he appeared at the Larrabee door properly appareled in an old long-tailed coat with satin revers, and fine cloth-topped calfskin boots, his short, stubby beard and fringe of white hair glistening like the snow he brought in on the old coonskin cap which protected his bald head.

My mother — younger than he by twenty years and more social by nature — met her hostess with a gleam of anticipatory excitement in her eyes, and a smile. I ran to her surging with delight and a new sense of appreciation. How *pretty* she was! How black her hair!

And how glad I was to see her! If she had asked me then and there to get my wraps and go home I would have gladly gone. And yet I had never before even been conscious of her appearance, and I know now that she was quite plain of face.

But she did not ask me to go home. She smiled at me, she patted my arm. My father gave me a comradely glance, and they were off to lay aside their things in a spare bedroom. I, being one of the younger fry, returned to the position of spectator of what to me was a gorgeous pageant of color, sound, and odor.

Largely, it seems to me now, this all had to do with food. There was, of course, the fanfare of noise: voices — young voices, children's voices, tender voices, shouting voices, frivolous, gay, commanding, fooling; the voices of serene, contented, assured people having a good time; voices that would never become ribald, because ribaldry was unknown; voices that would not thicken or blur as the evening progressed, because the beverages that were provided neither stimulated nor benumbed the tongue; the voices of sane, happy people who would not wake to remorse on the morrow, or become calloused beyond the reach of regret. Simple, uncultivated people, as culture is deemed to-day, but with a code of decency, not to say morality, and a few ideals of chastity and the sanctity of marriage and the home to which, in the main, they religiously conformed. If deluded, they enjoyed their delusions, which is more than can be said of those whose so-called modern nude realism offers neither enjoyment nor content.

We did not stay long that first Sunday night at the Larrabees', although even so my father's restless feet were held longer than either my mother or I had hoped. Nothing, however, — neither the comparative strangeness of his surroundings nor his avowed reluctance at being there, — could keep him from the kitchen. A kitchen, and the odors that emanated from it, were to my father's nose what the earth was to the Newton apple.

Ostensibly he came looking for his small daughter, who was, with Janey, happily engaged in picking meats from a pan of butternuts. At sight, however, of the number of youngsters milling about the kitchen and into the dining room beyond, hands laden with platters of cold ham, pans of beans, plates of biscuits, he would have attempted retreat, but they were upon him.

"Come on, Mr. Thompson," Elizabeth Larrabee called, "I want someone to open this bottle of pickles. None of these boys are strong enough."

To my dismay and amazement she was thrusting the jar into his unwilling hands, laughing, pushing him farther into the room while others paused to laugh. My father! Shy, and ever fearful of his dignity because of that shyness! Father, who hated all that he

called capering and cutting up, surrounded and play-
fully badgered by this gay hilarious crowd! It served
him right for poking his inquisitive nose into the
kitchen, but I could not bear it. It made me think
of a woodchuck I once saw cornered by some boys and
a dog.

Springing to my feet, — and so scattering the nuts
in a dozen ways, — I ran to him, grabbed him about
the knees, and sobbed, "Oh, Pa! Pa!"

Unintentioned as this panicky release was, it gave him
reason for escape. He thrust the jar of pickles into
the hands of some astonished bystander, took me by
the shoulders, and shook me.

"Stop it!" he ordered. "What's the matter with
you? Ain't you ashamed of yourself? Come along!"
Ingloriously he dragged me, not back through the
crowded rooms, but out the kitchen door and through
a woodshed.

"Don't believe I blanketed the horse," he announced
with utter irrelevance to the occasion. "Better see to
it." My hand warmly held in his, big and hard and full
of assurance, I trotted beside his striding legs to the
shed, where the horse was found, properly protected
and sociably greeting us with velvety nicker.

By the light of a flooding moon he hitched the
blanket here, hiked it a little there — and then we went
back to the house, entering unperceived, or at least
unnoticed, by the front door, and so into the parlor,

where instantly my mother's eye, piercingly suspicious but unquestioning, fell upon us.

In a few minutes the call to supper came, and, closely shepherding each other, we took our way to the long dining room.

Not every Sunday night, of course, in the Larrabee home, — as a later and more intimate acquaintance proved, — saw the long table stretched to its utmost, or its cloth laden with a plethora of food. On days when special company or a family gathering had occasioned a heavier and later dinner than usual, the evening's refreshments merely consisted of apples, cider, and doughnuts, popcorn or a taffy pull; or, on a very cold night, of hot soup and crackers, with cake and coffee to top off with. But, often enough to become a legend in the memories of those who have only memory upon which to make like feast, the Sunday-night supper in that hospitable home was a memorable affair.

In the first place, there was the table. Since there would be no knowing just how many would eventually draw around it, no attempt was made to *set* it properly, but it took time to prepare — and it took a lot of hands. No one sat off in the parlor waiting to be called to supper except Father and Mother Larrabee and their own guests. This Sunday-night supper was the young people's affair.

Laying the cloth, which would measure considerably

over three yards, took two to four pairs of hands to manage. The centre decoration called for deliberation. When flowers were scarce, a handsome cake often had the place of honor — a cake made specially for the purpose by one of the girls on Saturday; perhaps a round layer cake, oozing rich dark chocolate, with a smooth glazed coat of the same; a moist and velvety bed of cake resting on a high-posted dish of glass with a slightly rolled edge to keep the cake in place.

The matter of ornamentation settled, a pile of plates or two were placed on the table with silver beside them. Huge pitchers of milk — or, in season, sweet cider — and a pot of tea or chocolate went at one end, with, sometimes on a cold winter's night, a huge tureen of oyster soup at the other, and a dish of cole slaw at the side.

There would be, perhaps, a large pan of baked beans, lightly browned and with a slight exposure of the piece of scored salt pork that lent savory flavor to the dish. Beans for Sunday night, even if there had been beans for supper the Saturday night before. Michigan people did not easily tire of beans. They formed sort of a stabilizing background to the diet, as the oak groves did to the scenery.

There would be cold meat, — cold sliced ham smokily reminiscent of hickory stick and corncob; or headcheese smelling pungently of sage and spice; or a roast loin of fresh pork, the white slices rivaling in appearance and flavor the breast of turkey, — the kind of meat depending upon the season and the relative importance of the occasion. There would be plates of bread: bread baked in the huge oven of the old iron stove that had held more good food in its time than all the proud white beauties of to-day will ever boast; bread baked on Saturday and kept moist in a crock, its color suggestive of the creamy ears of wheat of which it was made, not too finely milled; bread made with 'east, and salt-risin' bread. And butter: butter in pound pats — one at each end of the table, stamped with a sheaf of wheat and placed in a silver dish with its accompanying knife properly slotted at the side.

There would be pickles — peach and pear pickles, glazed with the rich red juice which had preserved them, and bristling with cloves; watermelon pickle, ripe cucumber pickle, crab apples or currants spiced. Not all of these at once, naturally, but varying throughout the year.

Sometimes there were salads — the girls were learning newfangled ideas in town: salad of apple chopped with celery; potato salad in a dressing made rich with cream; chicken or salmon salad.

There were cookies, and always there were cakes — not only the one cake in the centre of the table, but other cakes as well. Devil's Food, and Angel's Food, pound cake for Father Larrabee, Lady Baltimore cake

for Mother Larrabee, whipped-cream cake for Henry —
and so on, week after week, until it seemed as if variety
were never staled.

And no one person in the family felt the burden of
preparation, not only because of the pleasure it brought
both in anticipation and in realization, but because it
was shared. Mother Larrabee allowed no one to attempt competition with her in the making of "riz"
biscuits. She made a batch three times a week and
counted an hour over the stove as only one of the
cheerful contributions of her time to the pleasure of
her family. Tildy cooked the beans and defied the
whole county to equal the results, although my own
personal opinion was that my mother's beans were, as
my father would have said, just a *lee*-tle mite tastier —
owing, I think, to the fact that, in addition to the pork
with which they were cooked, she always gave them a
generous touch of butter.

We were frequently invited to be present at Sunday-
night supper after this first incursion into the Larrabee
home. In fact, the Larrabees and my own people became quite intimate friends. But obdurately my father
held to his refusal to go capering over there at a time
when folks ought to be going to bed. Think he's going to chase off two miles just to *eat?* What think
he is? A *pig?* And as for staying around till all hours

the night to hear a lot of yawping around the organ —
no, sir! He's going to stay home and go to bed —
provided, of course, he could get anything to eat at
home.

And so, much as I yearned to be one of that gay, noisy
throng, and much as I knew my mother would also
have enjoyed a little of the festivity, we stayed at home
and went to bed.

Until one Sunday night just after Christmas. Mrs.
Larrabee and Elizabeth drove over during the week to
invite us. There was a whole huge roasted turkey,
they said, and it would take the entire neighborhood
to eat it up. My father was noncommittal as they
left, but after they were gone he gave his ultimatum.
No, sir! He was not going! He wasn't going to have
no ten-year-old daughter of *his* gaddin' off into that
crowd Sunday nights. What, he'd like to know, was
my mother thinking of? First thing *he* knew she'd
be traipsin' her off to a *dance!*

"So," said my mother, blandly, going about her work,
"you think you won't go."

"I *know* I won't go," he stormed. "No 'think' about
it. Biggest tarnation fool thing I ever heard of!"

"Well," interrupted my mother calmly, "*I'm* going.
You can stay home and take care of Delly if you don't
want her to go."

"Huh!" he said, smugly incredulous, and went out to
milk.

Panicky, I crept to my mother's lap. "Oh, Mother," I wept, "I don't *want* to stay home with Pa."

"Don't you worry," blithely admonished my mother, "till the time comes."

I had not much faith in her confidence, although I had seen my father weaken once before in the matter of a church supper, and even follow us upon another occasion to a Sunday School picnic under guise of a ruse too patent to fool a goose. But that he would ever change his mind, once asserted, about going out in the *evening* was too much to hope for.

The week wore on and Saturday came. My mother made her usual batches of bread, friedcakes, cookies, the pan of beans for Saturday's supper.

My father, going about his own work, paid little attention to the usual routine of cleaning, cooking, and general preparation for the Sabbath. He was engaged in splitting up some nice dry pitchy tamarack logs that would snap and crackle when put in the stove, and I helped him. Armful after armful of the prickly, odorous sticks was carried into the kitchen and piled in the old wood box beside the stove. When this would hold no more we laid it in the woodshed. It was a mild winter's day, snow falling gently upon a ground already white. Shep officiously gamboled before us as we walked. Odors, spicily sweet, floated out upon the sparkling air: odors that reminded me — but seemed to stir no like anticipatory reflections in my father's mind — of the invitation that was ours for to-morrow night, and of my mother's assertion that she, at least, should accept.

Nothing had been said during the entire week, so far as I knew, regarding it. Once, after ridding my arms of their load, I stood before my mother where she was sprinkling pink sugar on round, scalloped cookies and ventured to ask in tones muted to an open door, "You going over to Janey's to-morrow night, Ma? Won't Pa go?"

"I couldn't tell you," said my mother, breaking the whites of eggs into a bowl and whisking them vigorously with a fork, "whether he'll go or not. The less you say about it the better."

Saturday night saw the usual rituals performed. We ate our supper, we had our baths — at least my mother and I held rendezvous with the washtub in the kitchen. My father had already been closeted behind a door with much sound of splashed water and stentorian grunts.

We put on our clean nightgowns and crept into our clean, cold beds.

On Sunday morning there was the sound of my father's razor slipping, *slap-slap-slap,* against the strop a little earlier than usual. "You like to go over to church this mornin', 'Miry?" he asked genially. " 'S good sleighin' — and 't ain't cold."

My mother glanced quickly at him — breaking golden islands of egg into the crackling fat of roseate ham. "No," she said, blandly, "I guess I can't. I'm goin' to bake a cake this morning."

"Cake!" my father echoed, staring at her as if she had declared an intent to cook a whale. "What you want to bake a *cake* for? Did n't you bake yestiddy?"

"Yes," she said briefly, "I baked — but I did n't bake a cake."

She did not look at him. For a moment he stared after her, then drew his chair to the table. We ate.

After breakfast he said, "I guess I'll go over to Bouldrys' — see how his apples is holdin' out. You want to come, Delly?"

It was a poor excuse, but my mother made no remark. He hitched the horse to the cutter and we went over to Bouldrys', sleighbells tinkling to the slow jog of a horse too fat for his own good.

When we came back, several hours later, dinner was ready. So also was a perfect mountain of a cake. Indeed, as we later learned, it was called a White Mountain cake. A white miracle of a cake, four layers high, each layer mattressed with a thick frosty pudding of sweet crystal snow, befeathered, befluffed with flakes of coconut white as milk; and over it all an argent thatch of shaggy glacial white spurtling over the edges like freshets caught and held by fingers of the Queen of Snows.

"Ho!" said my father, sniffing, bending, staring. "A *coconut* cake! When's that for? Dinner?"

"No," said my mother blandly. "It's for supper."

"Whew!" said my father, whistling softly. "Jiminy! Seem's if I never saw a purttier cake. Why don't we have it now?"

"Because," explained my mother breezily, "we've got pie for dinner. Mince."

"Well," said my father, with what upon mature reflection I am convinced was false assurance, "I guess I won't fill up *too* much on pie."

"I would n't," said my mother, "if I was you."

I felt sorry for him, for I knew that he liked coconut cake particularly, and I wished my mother would give him some.

To this day I do not know whether my father *had* forgotten the forthcoming crisis or whether he and my mother were matching wits. All I know is that the afternoon wore away in restlessness. Old Man Covell came over to borrow a go-devil with which to split a stubborn log, and he and my father spent some time at the barn — a longer time than my father was wont to spend with his shiftless, borrowing neighbor, whose ways he so thoroughly disliked. Then Covell went home and my father went about his chores.

Evening approached — and dark. With no explanations, my mother set the huge beautiful cake in a big basket and threw a towel over it. She called me into the kitchen, brushed my hair, and helped me change my dress to my very best, a dark blue cashmere with fine red braid and bright buttons. My mother had on her brown alpaca and gold brooch with red coral in it. My heart quaked so that I could not speak. Questions were beyond me.

My father came in, set the milk on the table. My mother tied an apron about her waist, took the milk into the pantry and strained it. Shivering and prickly with apprehension, I watched my father. His blue eyes looked dark, his lips were thin.

"Where you goin'?" he asked, with some feeble attempt at lightness, as she came out.

"Me?" Mother looked at him brightly — but her voice was like slivers of ice in the horses' tracks. "Oh, I'm goin' over to Larrabees' to supper. Delly's goin', too."

My father walked over to the stove, lifted a lid, poked the fire. It was almost out. The teakettle barely steamed.

"Well," he said, finally, "how you goin'?"

"Oh, I'll drive," said my mother, her voice still clinking. "I thought maybe you'd hitch up for us."

"You mean to tell me," he turned upon her sternly, his ruddy cheeks almost pale, "you'd drive off over there *yourself*, after dark?"

"Why, yes," said my mother, still tinkling brightly, "I would. I'd have to — unless you come along. Don't hit that basket — the cake's in there."

The look he gave her was that of a stricken boy of

fourteen whose baseball bat has been taken away and given to a rival.

"You takin' that coc'nut cake over there?" he demanded. But it was more of a suspicion confirmed than a question asked.

"Why, yes," said my mother, busy with hoods, coats, and arctics, "of course I be. That's what I made it for."

He stood, immobile as the big black stove beside him, for what seemed to me at least an unconscionable time. What *might* he do, his brows thundering, his eyes reproaching?

Then slowly he went to his bedroom. In a little while he came out, the cloth-topped, calfskin boots on his feet, the old long-tailed coat on his back. He put on his shabby overcoat, picked up his coonskin cap and his knitted mittens, and at the door turned an accusing face toward my mother.

"Come to a pretty pass," he said stonily, "if a man's got to get out *bedtime* and go to the neighbors to get anything fit to eat." He went out and shut the door.

But my mother only laughed. "Put on your scarf," she said to me lightly, "and come along. Chances are he's got the horse all harnessed."

One marvels, in pausing to sink for a moment of recollection back into the luxury of such days as those,

how people ate so much. Or *did* they eat so much?
Or was there huge waste?

What we, in our lean hours of economic striving,
would call waste, of course there was. The whites of
eight eggs to make one cake were not at all an unusual
rule. Half a cup of butter was tossed here and there
with the lavish gesture of a child flinging sand. That
was waste of a kind — but who cared? Left-overs were
used up to the point of desirability, but there were always any number of four-footed animals eagerly waiting to dispose of what their two-legged brothers scorned.

And whether at the table people *ate* what was put before them or not, they wanted to see it there. It was
part of the manner of living that the table should indi-
cate both the worldly status of a farmer's life and the
professional standing of his wife. For in that day a
good farmer's wife admittedly considered that being a
good housewife was the whole of her career, and if she
was a good housewife she had to be a good cook. Some
were better than others. Some were especially skilled
in one form of cookery, some in another. But *cooking*,
more than any other form of housewifery, was where a
woman came closest to the expression of herself in an
art.

Miz' Bouldry, for instance, was a master hand at
cakes. She made a fig layer cake that would have got
her a passport into Heaven if Saint Peter had a sweet
tooth. My own mother could not be surpassed at

strawberry shortcake, but she also excelled in the heartier courses, such as stuffed spareribs, Irish stew with dumplings, or a crisply golden loin of pork baked to perfection, redolent of sage and served with mashed turnip (yellow, not white), potato, and the boat of gravy smooth as molasses and brown as an acorn's shell.

Tildy's creative forte lay in the construction of pies. Not better than my mother's, whose rhubarb, apple, pumpkin, and mince beat a rhythmic homophony through the seasons, but equal to hers; and the making done, I have thought since, in a different mood. My mother would sometimes breathe a sigh when she had to go in from a wistful contemplation of summer mists withdrawing flimsily over the meadow before the militant advance of a braggart sun. But she would go in, and she would peel the thin skin from a Yellow Harvest with a steady knife and weld the crisp, juicy portions into a luscious filling bedded below and coverleted above with such crust as the Elysian ovens might burst with envy to behold. And if her eyes wandered to the window, the meadow, the high-riding sun, and the fleeting mists, her fingers never stumbled in their cunning, nor did her spirit lose its poise.

But Tildy had no thought of mists or meadows either to console or to distract. Her mind was on her immediate business, and while her technique was no better than my mother's, and her results by no means superior, she perhaps got more pleasure out of her work.

With Tildy, cooking and housework were *all* of woman's business in life. With my mother, — if I may judge by reflection rather than by childish observation, — cooking and housekeeping happened to be her business *at that time*, and she attended these to the best of her stretched ability. She never complained or rebelled, and if she had thoughts about this business she kept them to herself. Now, however, I think she had thoughts.

With such standards, then, of hospitality, to say nothing of such needs for plentiful provision, the laying of the table on a Sunday night at the Larrabee home, when a regular supper was in order, might safely be left to the imagination, if, that is, one has had sufficient experience with such lush provision to visualize the picture. Only those whose youth was spent in such localities are able to envisage the "groaning table" as it was seen in many a Mid-Western town during those abundant years following upon the tragedy of war.

Price? Yes, there was a price on such a supper that we, with all our luxuries, cannot afford to pay. Butter and cream and eggs, the ingredients that lend flavor and richness to food, were just a part of the ordinary living of that day. It is difficult for one raised amongst such plenty to see the economy of selling, as farmers do nowadays, every quart of milk to buy a niggardly pound of butter in return. One wonders just what *kind* of economy it is. What have we lost in the spirit of hospitality, of gracious and generous living, to gain the conveniences and so-called luxuries of to-day?

With memories such as these how can one hope to bring to the cramped and narrow board of the present any semblance of that benevolent living which once made our countryside so gracious and friendly a place? Food had a good deal to do with it — no doubt about that. The women who made the homes in that day held no false notions about the worth of food in moulding not only the physical life of man but the spiritual life as well. They gave much of their time and thought and strength to the preparation of food and counted the expenditure good. Most of those women are gone or have been made to feel by the invasion of modern trends that their usefulness as homemakers is ended, their methods antiquated. The generations that have intervened, thrown from the orbit of homemaking, as the older women knew it, by inventions and innovations, have turned their backs upon the kitchen. So-called "larger interests" have absorbed them until the blessing of hospitality has all but fled the house, and the pleasure and satisfaction once found in the growing, preserving, and preparation of food are all but lost.

IV

Jodie Acts As Pallbearer

PASSING the Covell place on my way to school one windy, cold, and cloudy day in early March when I was about ten years old, I saw Ol' Man Covell come out of his door and swing down the road ahead of me, his shabby old coat flapping about his lean legs, a wool cap pulled low upon his head. Just behind him came three of his daughters with tin dinner pails in their hands. They waited for me, eager with news.

"Pa's goin' down to Bouldrys'," they said, "to get Jodie for a pallbearer."

The word was a new one to me and so I stumbled along, my own pail swaying, my feet stumbling on the frozen ruts, so put to it I was to meet their pace.

"You know what a pallbearer is?" Amarita, the eldest, demanded, shrewdly suspecting my silence. I shook my head.

"Well, it's carryin' somebody that's dead."

Clumsily my toes stubbed against a hummock of icy mud. I staggered and dropped my pail. The lid flew off, but a neatly folded square of cloth kept the food

from spilling. The Covells paused, but excitement over
the adventure about to face Jodie Bouldry overcame
what would otherwise have become a lively interest in
its contents.

"Hurry up," Amarita admonished. "We want to hear
what he says."

We trotted along in the footsteps of Covell sire, and
overtook him just as he had caught hold of young Jodie
tearing out of the Bouldry gate. Panting, open-mouthed,
we paused to hear.

Little Jodie stood squarely before him, his small,
stubby, copper-toed, cowhide boots slightly spraddled,
the better to support his shocked and apprehensive legs,
his dinner pail held in a rigid hand. What in time,
he wondered, did Ol' Covell want with him? *He* had n't
done nothin'.

Mr. Covell looked exceedingly grave, not to say solemn. Always his face was long, but now it was grim.

"The Bishops' baby died last night," he said heavily.
"Tom Bishop was just over to tell us."

Jodie's blue eyes widened. His sandy hair, harshened
and erratically bleached by country winds and sun, and
ruled by a stubborn cowlick, seemed to rise in amazed
denial.

"The Bishops ain't *got* no baby," he said, not by way
of contradiction, but as correcting an error. "I 's there
just last night on th' way home from school. They ain't
got only Benjy."

"They *had* a baby," Mr. Covell told him soberly. "It come in the night to Miz' Bishop and it died this morning. The funeral's to-morrow. Two o'clock. They want you to be a pallbearer."

Jodie's blue eyes stared into his neighbor's face, in each a blazing spark burning wildly beneath the startled brows. Jodie was just turned nine and small for his age. He had never been a pallbearer, but, as was discovered later, he knew boys who had. "Big fellers, fifteen — sixteen; that time when Milt Green cut his leg on a scythe and gangrene set in. Even *girls*. When Milly Brant died of the fever, the' was six girls, but they was big girls, too." Never had there been, to his knowledge, little boy pallbearers. But then, never, so far as he knew, had there been so little a baby to bury.

" — And Miz' Bishop wants four little boys for pallbearers, — the coffin won't weigh hardly nothin', — all about you and Benjy's age. Tom left the hull thing to me," Mr. Covell added, not boastfully, but as one professionally acquainted with the accoutrements of Death, "except he specified they wanted Benjy, and he said Miz' Bishop herself asked for you. Because you 'n' Benjy's such good friends."

Jodie's small slight figure imperceptibly expanded with, as you might say, a spiritual inflation. His blue eyes glowed, the brown freckles across his stub nose stood out against the wind-burned skin like the seeds of a milkweed pod. His copper toes moved in anticipatory consciousness of the morrow's solemn tread.

"That Barlow boy's about your age, ain't he?"

"Fred? Ayunh. He's past nine, but he's bigger 'n me."

"That don't matter. He ain't much bigger. An' the's Dan Blake's boy."

"Ayunh. His name's Dan, too."

"Be to school, won't they?"

"Ayunh."

"Fetch 'em back with you to my house this afternoon. I got to give you all a little schoolin' in how to act. Git along now, and see 't you're back early." An admonition entirely superfluous.

Old Covell, in spite of all his shiftlessness, was a pretty good neighbor in one way. He liked to sit up with the dead and he was a master hand at laying them out. There was no real undertaker nearer than Jackson, and if the roads did n't happen to be drifted in winter or almost impassable with ruts in spring, they were deep with sand in summer and people had to be laid out before you could get the undertaker there. Besides, nobody would ever think of paying an undertaker to lay out their dead. That was one of the exchange courtesies of neighborliness.

Old Covell sometimes hung wallpaper, too, for folks that could n't do it themselves, and he had a wide board that he laid across two "horses" to spread the paper on for the application of paste. He used the same board as a kind of bier on which to lay the corpse before the coffin came.

It was only men that he took care of, of course. Most always folks would send for my mother when a child or a woman died, but Old Covell took care of the men. He wasn't worth a cent to sit up with the sick (any more than my father was). He'd get up — if it was summer — and go outside to smoke his pipe, and fall asleep somewhere. In winter he would stick his stockinged feet in the oven, and shortly doze. But a dead man seemed to rouse some sense of responsibility in him as did nothing else. He never wore a necktie himself in his life, and he never was seen with a boot on his foot until it got so cold he'd freeze if he didn't wear them. But when he had a body to lay out he would command the best pants and holler if he found a hole in a sock, although when *he* wore socks you could see the calluses on his foot through the heel. He'd polish the boots and put on a white shirt and a collar and fasten a little black tie to the collar button in front. He actually kept some of these neckties on hand and a box of celluloid collars to put on when the man wasn't too old.

My mother said she bet he wasn't any too fussy about *washing* the corpses, but he did a good job at dressing them up and he took a pride in it. When he'd got one all dressed, its hair brushed and moustache or beard brushed out, he'd lay a wide piece of black cloth he had over the board and put the body on it. My father said he kept this piece of cloth in the barn along with his old horse blankets, and that there was never any danger of smelling anything else because the blanket stunk so. My mother told him he always stretched things and he ought to be ashamed of himself and give Ol' Covell the credit for doing *one* thing well, anyway, but my father told her the next time she went to where Covell had laid a man out to hold her nose open and see *what* she smelled.

It was not often that Covell was called upon to supervise the funeral of a child, but poor Tom Bishop, as my mother said when discussing the matter at supper, must have been about wild. The woman they had expected to attend Miz' Bishop hadn't come on account of the baby being beforehand, and Tom had put in an awful time, though he had got Miz' Lury Lane, who lived next them on the west road, when she was took bad. My mother had taken food over and stayed there most of the day. I think she may not have liked it very well that Mr. Bishop had preferred Old Covell to her, but then, as she said to Miz' Bouldry afterward, if Miz' Bishop hadn't been too sick to have any say in it, things 'd been different. But of course, Old Covell could run a funeral and she couldn't.

My father said that anybody must be crazy that wanted Ol' Covell around and that if *he* should die and they brought Ol' Covell and his wallpaper board in, he 'd get up and walk out, dead or alive.

Old Covell, however, was now full of the importance of his mission and strode off toward home and a busy day.

Jodie apparently worried a little for fear Benjy would have forestalled him with the stupendous piece of information which burned his breast. But Benjy was not at school. The decorum of family bereavement had not yet penetrated Jodie's experience.

He set for us a fierce pace along the muddy, rutty half mile to school, with hardly a word. It was a low-ering day, having rained at night, and a raw March wind whipped the bare branches of maples against each other and stirred faint ripples in the puddles along the road. His tin dinner pail swinging from one bare red hand, the other cutting back and forth in accom-panying rhythm, his copper-toed boots squshing through seeping Michigan sand or sopping roadside grass, Jodie covered the flat, uninteresting distance between his home and the schoolhouse in record time, all but bursting with the importance of his mission. And when, breathless, panting from the last final spurt of speed, he came within sight of the schoolhouse and the boys playing outside, he was practically beyond speech. His face was crimson with racing blood. His cap hung precariously to one ear and the lock of hair most prominently controlled by the cowlick drooped, dripping with perspiration, over one eye. The right leg of his pants had escaped from his boot top and was encrusted with slush. We, as escort extraordinary, were winded and spent.

Espying his unsuspecting colleagues of the morrow, he shouted their names: "C'm'ere, Danny. Hi, Freddy — c'm'ere. I got suthin' to tell you — "

But cutting in upon the planned oratorical presentation of his theme came the strident clamor of the bell. The teacher, a young woman obviously intent upon a roll of the living rather than disposition of the dead, stood swinging the raucous tongue of brass censerlike upon the leaden air until the last straggler had filed past her into the door. That last one was Jodie, still hopeful of a moment's consultation with his peers. That privilege denied him, he waited feverishly until the roll was called, when, the ritual over, his hand shot into the air.

"Please, teacher, c'n me 'n Danny Blake go after a pail o' water?" "Going after the water" was a privilege usually accorded the virtuous.

It had been difficult for Jodie to decide upon which of his cohorts he should first confer the favor of such an honor. Danny sat farthest away. Freddy was just across the aisle. A surreptitious message *might* reach Freddy before recess, so Danny was chosen.

Jodie was a good little boy and Danny happened to be in present favor, so the request was granted.

"And come right straight back," adjured the teacher, "so 's to get at your geography lesson. You missed on it yesterday."

Their return was prompt, not so much as a measure of obedience but the quicker to get the word across to Freddy. And between them they had formulated a plan whereby to hasten the hour in which Mr. Covell was to initiate them into the etiquette of pallbearing. The plan, too, would admit of a spectacular means by which to inform not only Freddy but the whole school of what miraculous fate had befallen the chosen four. The water pail, woefully lacking in measure owing to ebullience of excitement affecting arms and legs, was hurriedly placed upon the bench. Teacher was at that moment fortuitously dismissing the first class in reading. Jodie's copper-toed boots strode valiantly to a place just before the rostrum on which stood teacher's desk and chair. His red, chapped, cold little hand shot from a too short sleeve to a point level with her eye.

"Well, Jodie, what is it?" Teacher was slightly impatient. Jodie was becoming a nuisance.

"Please, ma'am, me and Danny and Freddy Barlow" (a quick, gloating look over his shoulder at the goggle-eyed Freddy, startled at this sudden rendering of his name) "and Benjy Bishop 's all goin' to be pallbearers to-morrow, only Benjy ain't here, and please, ma'am, we can't none of us stay after school because Ol' Man Covell — "

"*Pall*bearers!" Teacher's incredulous voice cut in upon the incoherent flow of words, her amazement overshadowing even the usual pedagogical proneness to correct improper and disrespectful speech. "What do you mean, Jodie? What about pallbearers?"

"Yes'm. We 're pallbearers for the Bishops' baby — "

"The Bishops' *baby!*" By this time curiosity had the entire school in its fevered grip. "*What* baby?"

"They had a baby. It came in the night — last night. Tom Bishop was over to Covells' this morning, early, to tell Mr. Covell. But it died. The funeral 's to-morrow. Two o'clock. And we 're pallbearers. And Mr. Covell wants to learn us something. We got to get there early."

Restiveness in the room, due to suppressed eagerness, recalled the teacher to present obligations.

"Very well," she said with what quietude came to her command, "you and Freddy and Danny may all go home promptly. Now go back to your seat and get to work — all of you."

Four o'clock found the four little boys gathered around Mr. Covell's chair in the kitchen, and also all the Covell girls, with their little neighbor, Delly, who at their urgent invitation promptly ignored an established rule for coming directly home and not dawdling. Benjy Bishop had come over to partake of the necessary instructions in funeral etiquette. They sat perched on the edges of wooden chairs, their woolly caps held in grubby little paws resting on their knees, their copper-toed boots, wet and muddy, planted squarely upon the floor, their eager eyes fastened on Mr. Covell's face.

"I don't s'pose," said Mr. Covell, speaking gravely as a man to men upon a solemn occasion, " 't you 've noticed particular how pallbearers do, but the 's certain things you have to be sure about because — well, you do.   Now, one thing," he turned slightly in his chair to fix an inquisitorial eye upon the four small figures tensed upon four hard chairs — "you all got Sunday suits, ain't you?"

Four heads nodded eagerly.   Danny said, "Yessir." Jodie said, "Ayunh."

"Well, you want to git yerselves clean.   Wash behind yer ears and up onto yer wrists."   Four pairs of critical eyes stealthily appraised their advisor's own rather smudged appearance and four pairs of grimy hands guiltily withdrew into shrunken sleeves.

"And shine yer — you *got* shoes, ain't you?   Besides yer boots?"

Freddy Barlow signified such possession with justifiable pride.   His cowhide shoes were almost new.   And they had n't copper toes, either.   He had been one of those chosen to speak a piece at the school exhibition Christmas time and the shoes were bought for that occasion.

Danny's head drooped.   His father had cut his foot chopping timber early in the winter, so there had been little wood sold and money had been scarcer than usual. His mother had not even been able to get his old shoes resoled.   And until now there had been no special need.

Benjy Bishop looked vague. All this matter of birth and death and sudden fame was too much for him. He could not remember the condition of the shoes he had worn to the Sunday School picnic last summer and to the County Fair in September, but he felt reasonably sure of such possession.

Jodie nodded doubtfully. His copper toes were a recent acquisition, he was proud of them, and he did n't see why they were n't good enough for a funeral — of all things!

"Don't make no great matter," Mr. Covell was saying comfortably. "It 'll be muddy goin' even if it don't rain. Wear your boots, all of you, but clean 'em up and grease 'em to-night with goose grease or skunk's oil, whichever. Shine up the toes with ashes and pull yer pants down over the tops.

"Now, what you *do*. The casket 'll stand in the front room on a board 't we 'll put acrost ho'ses. I 'll look after that. The funeral's at two, and you want to be all ready by one-thutty. You won't set in the room with the co'pse. Tom and the relations and neighbors 'll set in there and I 'm goin' to have you set in the next room right by the door.

"Now when the minister goes through, I 'll be standin' in the door — you get up and put on yer overcoats, and march into the room. You first, Freddy — you 're tallest; then Danny, then Benjy, and you, Jodie, last. Keep yer caps in yer hands. And yer — *there!* I plumb forgot about — "

He paused, a slight frown troubling his brows. This business of outfitting amateurs was a little trying. "Pall-bearers," he said worriedly, "always wears gloves. We 've got some for men, but — well, you 'll just have to keep on your mittens. Le's see 'em." Four pairs of mittens in varying stages of wear, coloring, and repair were dragged from four sets of pockets. Ol' Man Covell eyed them dubiously.

"Well," he said with acceptance of the inevitable, "we got to get along with what we got. But — keep 'em on. Now," telling off the steps with the finger of one hand on the horny palm of another, "you march in to where the casket is. The baby 's so little we ain't goin' to let folks view the remains. I 'll nod to you when. The coffin 'll set east to west, the foot nearest the door. Freddy, you march to the first handle on the left. The one torge the door. Danny, you stand right behind Freddy. Benjy, you take the front right-hand handle, and Jodie the last. I 'll show you just how when you git there.

"Now, as soon as you take a-holt of the handle, you lay your caps on the casket. Just about so far apart. You got that?"

Solemnly, four small heads nodded — fair, dark, sandy, red.

"Now you march out. Keep step — left, *right;* left, *right* — we 'll practise that to-morrow. And be awful careful when you go down the steps. 'T won't be heavy, — the coffin won't weigh *nothin'*, — but your mittens might slip. I wisht you had gloves, but you ain't. And don't stub your toes. We 'll have the democrat wagon hauled right up to the ho'se block, tail end to, and you c'n h'ist 'er right in. I 'll be clost by. I 'll say 'One — two — three — *h'ist,*' sort of under my breath — so." The count was hoarsely breathed from a twisted corner of his mouth. "Tom Bishop and me 'll go along in the democrat. Three of you can ride in the back seat, and one with us. We 'll lead th' procession.

"Now," telling off another step, "when we get to th' cemet'ry, there 's quite a little step to go. Bishops' lot is over by the fence, — we 're goin' over in the morning to dig the grave, — but it 's a good gravel path and you 'll git along all right.

"You can put on yer caps when you git in the buggy after you 've h'isted the coffin in, but take 'em off again when you lift it out, and lay 'em on top. You set the coffin down beside the grave — I 'll be right there — and don't forget to take 'em off'n it. When you take 'em off'n it, hold 'em in your right hands up against yer hearts while the minister 's prayin' — like this" — picking up a battered old felt from off the floor, he rose vigorously to his feet and stood stiffly at attention, his right arm flung across his breast, his hand clasping the hat. It was truly amazing how much unsuspected energy Old Covell could muster upon occasion. Only death could call it to life.

The pallbearers were awed, impressed, and considerably

scared. This pallbearing business was not all fame and glory, as it had seemed to be.

"Now," Mr. Covell clapped the old felt to his head with a gesture of dismissal, "don't ferget what I 've told you. It 's a terrible solemn thing you got to do and I want you should do it right. You better hurry 'long home now; they might need you."

There was no school for the four pallbearers, even in the morning, on the eventful day. Freddy lived at the greatest distance and was successful in convincing his parents that a mile walk each way was hardly worth the shoe leather so employed, just to attend one 'rithmetic lesson which he already knew by heart. Anyways, it was only review.

Danny was half ill with excitement after Mr. Covell's lecture and had to be dosed with catnip tea. Jodie was needed to run errands between his own home and the Bishop place, and Benjy was already immune. The Covell girls, greatly to their chagrin and disgust, were sent off, but without the customary dinner pail. Miz' Covell was going early over to Bishops' to help in household affairs, and would take them along. I, also, accompanied my parents, although much against my father's wishes.

"No place to take her," he censured my mother as she dressed me. "If you don't want to leave her alone, *I 'll* stay with her. You can ride along with Bouldrys."

"You 'll come along," my mother told him briefly. "Look pretty, would n't it, you to stay home. 'T won't hurt 'er, and anyway you can keep 'er outdoors if you want to."

In a panic lest he should, I clung feverishly to my mother's hand, and she, mistaking curiosity for timidity, led me with her into the very room where the tiny casket stood, where we sat with other of the neighbors and the bereaved father. In the sitting room next, where the Bishops ate when "comp'ny" came, the pallbearers huddled by the door.

The minister was there, whispering solemnly with Mr. Covell — elegant now in a long-tailed rusty coat which I heard my father say in later capitulation of the event, had been given him with a bundle of rags by someone in the city where he sometimes gathered offal for his hogs. The singers — Miz' Lou Esty, soprano, and Miz' Lury Lane, alto — were thumbing the hymnbook.

The pallbearers, scrubbed to a shining luminosity, sweated and itched in the hot room. It was too early to discard winter underclothes, and their long-legged, long-sleeved, fleece-lined shirts and drawers tormented their worried flesh. Their hot, chapped hands felt as if thrust into a fiery furnace. Jodie, his small fingers twitching miserably in their woolly encasement, discovered a hole in one thumb and surreptitiously pushed and poked until the little red digit felt the heavenly contact with outer air. His heels, recently bitten by a lingering frost, burned as if stung by a thousand nettles and nervously he rubbed them, one against the other, upon the rungs of his chair. In school next day these sufferings were related with no loss of detail.

In agony they listened to the droning voice of the old minister, who dwelt upon the blessedness of an uncontaminated life. Hopefully they heard the humming sound of the singers' voices striking their harmony, and then the lifting of doleful strains that dealt with the regenerative blood of the Lamb.

But their hearts sank again as the minister entered upon his supplication for the safety of the departed soul. However, there is an end to all things, even the reluctant consignment of a life still dewy-winged in its flight from a recent Heaven, and soon there was Mr. Covell nodding and signaling at the door, and into the waiting hush the pallbearers marched (left, *right* — left, *right*).

Their fuzzy, woolly caps — red, red and black, blue and red, orange and black — were decorously placed upon the white lid, their mittened hands grasped the silver drops with the intensity of aching fear. *"What if I should stub my toe! What if I should lose my holt!"* But no one lost his "holt," no one stubbed a toe.

At the grave they laid their precious burden down beside the pine box that would protect it from the immediate crassness of its mother earth. They picked up their worn woolly caps and as one man pressed them to their thumping hearts.

Miz' Bouldry and Jodie rode home with us. They would wait at our house until Mr. Bouldry, who had stayed to help cover the grave, came along. Jodie and I went to the barn to help my father with the chores.

There were some bags of grain in the barn which my father was transferring to a wagon, and which would be delivered to-morrow. Jodie watched my father rather laboriously shoulder a bag and shuffle with it to the wagon, breathing deeply. Suddenly he broke his stance, took a step forward, and laid a hand upon the wheel.

"Want I sh'd he'p you load this grain, Mr. Thompson?" he asked genially, after the manner of men who share burdensome work upon a farm.

My father turned and looked at him, surprise and then amusement breaking over his features. He threw back his head and Jovian laughter smote the air.

"Think you could heft one of these here bags?" he grinned. "Must be feelin' pretty big."

Jodie took his hand from the wheel, drove both fists deeply into his pockets. His copper toes glistened widely against the sodden earth.

"Well," he said, becoming dignity tinged with justifiable indignation, "I been a pallbearer, ain't I?"

V

Remember the Sabbath

THE farming community of which Southern Michigan was composed some fifty or sixty years ago was not, I should say, a particularly religious one, but the village churches were reasonably well attended, Ladies' Aid Societies and Sewing Circles formed a considerable part of the social life, and Sunday, whether for spiritual, social, or other reasons, was a day universally observed as being different from others.

In my own home, the groundwork, as you might say, for observation of the Sabbath was laid on Friday. On that day the house was cleaned, all but the kitchen floor, which would be scrubbed the very last thing after the baking was done on Saturday. On Friday night the beans would be put to soak, the bread to rise. But on Saturday morning the real preliminaries began. Bread and beans were baked, doughnuts fried. On Saturday, too, in preparation for the morrow's dinner, some sacrificial offering from the poultry yard was often made. Especially was this true if company seemed imminent, or perchance in the fall when there was a preponderance of cocks, or in the spring when one of the hens persisted in the will-to-brood.

Now, a hen's will-to-brood is one of the most stubborn and obdurate traits of bird nature. The hen is a stupid creature at best, obviously lacking reasoning power, and perversely given to doing the very thing she especially should not — as witness her propensity for crossing roads in the face of danger. The hen, that is, that was part of the country life of which I write. The modern hen seems to have acquired the general feminine tendency to eschew all maternal responsibilities whatever, since the introduction of the incubator into her natural realm. The late hours she is made to keep and the unnatural forcing of her productive powers tend to destroy that quality of leisurely regard in which she once held her own maternity. Her entire manner of life has changed, and with it her once dull and obstinate, but pleasantly dawdling, nature. Instead of having, even in the proper season, any undue urge to perpetuate her kind, or to cause annoyance by a too persistent inclination in that direction, she seems, like her less befeathered sisters, to be ever on the restless move, unstable, capricious, and utterly lost to the tenets and traditions of her progenitors.

In my mother's day, however, a hen was the natural — and only — means of hatching, as well as of providing, the egg. She also dwelt in full recognition of that fact, and made the most of it. When she had rid herself of the usual allotment of properly fecundated ova, she went to the nest where she had deposited them and where she expected to find them, and sat. If you wanted chickens you encouraged her. If you did not, and preferred that she carry on in the rôle of producer, you tried to break her of it.

One of my mother's methods of ridding her of the idea of maternal obligation was to douse her in a pail of water. This was supposed, one assumes, to cool her ardor, but too frequently it failed of the purpose and she would be found damp and surly, but determinedly brooding.

Another method was to tie a long white string to her leg, — a few yards from a ball of carpet rags usually served the purpose, — and sometimes she would become so intent on trying to free herself that she would forget the nest. When all such simple expedients failed, the only thing left was to cut off her head.

Naturally a hen who had been for a week or more pitting her will against that of a still more obdurate creature would not be in the best condition for human consumption. As an excuse for dumplings or biscuits and gravy, however, she gave reasonably satisfactory returns.

And so either a superfluous cock or a hen paying the penalty for lack of intelligence or coöperation, or both, would be beheaded on the stained and feather-indented block out in the chip yard, scalded, plucked, drawn, and hung in the woodshed for the Sunday dinner. Of course in hot weather the execution would not take place until morning, when the early Sabbath quiet was pierced by protesting squawks.

Pies, in the season of fresh fruit, were generally made in the morning also, for my father liked his not too long from the oven, and my mother agreed with him that a day-old fruit pie was not fit to eat. Aside from these two possible exemptions, the main preparations for the nourishment of the family were made on Saturday.

These out of the way, my mother gave herself over to redding up the house, changing the beds, laying out clean clothing, and finally to getting the Saturday-night meal. This, while not such a rigidly held custom as in New England, was nevertheless a matter of some routine and tradition. There were, for one thing, the beans. Drained of the liquid in which they had been boiled, and baked with a neatly scored and crisply browned slab of salt pork embellishing the centre, they came from the oven gently hummocked in golden bronze, fragrant and hot. These would be accompanied by ketchup made in our own kitchen, where, against smoked rafters, the spicy and pungent odor of its making still lingered, not distinguishable of itself, but mingled with a thousand others reminiscent of summer days when pickling and preserving were the housewife's chief consideration — and joy.

Riz biscuits there would be also. We did not feel in duty bound to eat brown bread with our beans, as is the New England custom, for, in the first place, the beans themselves were not brown, but a nice, creamy, mealy white, sufficiently cohesive to allow slicing when cold. And for another thing, my father had definitely and pithily expressed his opinion and prejudices on the matter of bread. "When I git to where I got to eat hoss feed," he said, "I'll take it in the manger 'long with the hosses. But when I eat bread, I want *bread!*" And by "bread" he meant salt-rising bread and no other. And he wanted it fresh, with butter applied in no parsimonious mood. He did like riz biscuits, however, for a change, and so on Saturday nights these were taken from the swaddling towels in which they had been wrapped as they came from the oven, and laid, a nest of twelve hot, fragrant, crusty rounds, upon a plate.

With these there was honey — honey from our own hives, which my father had taken with bare hands from the unprotesting bees. There would also be pear or peach pickles resting in shallow pools of their own luscious amber juice, or some other relish from the brown and gray jars standing row upon row on the cellar shelves. Cup cakes, pound cake, or my father's favorite spice cake with seasonable or canned sauce would top the meal. Cake and sauce were a customary finish to the meal universally known as "supper."

This repast over and the dishes done, the Saturday-night bath was in order. And the arguments and controversies that arose over it still lie, warm and amusing, in my memory. These, of course, had to do with my father's part in the ceremony — if he had consented to have one, for both my mother and I accepted the obligation with the same degree of finality that we did the succession of Sunday after Saturday.

Of course we had neither bathroom nor bathtub. Neither had anyone else in that community or in any other, so far as I know, in all Southern Michigan. City folk somewhere may have had such innovations — indeed, later revelations as reported by Miz' Lou Esty, who sewed for city folks as well as for us of humbler means, indicated that such was the case. But we were not city folks. We were just plain farmers in what was known as ordinary circumstances. Our conveniences were extremely limited and such facilities as are now comfortably confined to the narrow stricture of four handsomely decorated walls were considerably scattered. For the more urgent needs there was the rudely constructed shelter situated some way back from the house at the end of what was in winter a precariously slippery plank walk, and in summer was modestly shielded from view by a rank growth of sunflowers and Jerusalem artichokes. A crude device, indeed, compared to the glass-and-chromium recess now devoted to the same universal need.

For the more formal ablutionary procedure we had

the china washbowl and pitcher in the spare bedroom, with soap dish and other accessories sacred to the use of company and the schoolma'am. These stood on a piece of furniture known as a commode, inside the lower compartment of which was another of the same pattern not mentioned in polite society. This, and the accompanying jar which stood on the floor at the side of the commode, had a crocheted hood, not so much for the purpose of decoration as a contribution to the accepted rules of modesty. For the schoolma'am or a visiting girl to have made a clatter, however mild, with either device would have brought the blush of shame to her cheek.

The larger ewer was filled with rain water (strained of wigglers) from barrel or cistern, and a smaller one was taken out by the hostess at night to be filled with hot water and brought to the guest-room door in the morning by host or hostess, according to the sex of the visitor — a welcome dispensation on a zero morning when the heel of a shoe was required to break the ice in the pitcher.

For family and general use there was the tin washbasin standing on the bench that held a cake of homemade soap in a brown earthenware dish, with a roller towel hanging from the wall, and an all-purpose comb reposing on a shelf beneath the looking-glass.

But for the special bath on Saturday night, water was heated in the wash boiler or in kettles on top of the stove, the wooden tub was brought in and set on the kitchen floor and filled for each in turn. One after another the family disrobed, stepped into the tub, lathered himself or herself (or was lathered, according to years) with soap specially refined for personal use and scented with sassafras root. The bather then squatted down as best he could, depending on his proportions and the condition of his joints, to "rench" off the suds. A child could manage such contortions very well, his objections being based solely upon the natural antipathy of the young toward useless effort. Just exactly how inconvenient an oversized and stiff-jointed adult found the performance would be difficult to say, since it would have been considered the essence of indecency for one person to reveal himself to another as God made him.

My father — I judge from fragmentary memories — seemed to feel that such childish custom not only was an insult to his stiffening joints and rather stocky form, but an offense to his dignity. My mother, it would seem, should have grown discouraged in the effort to convert him to her views on sanitation and left him to whatever unique devices he had for personal cleanliness, but she never did. Being of Dutch descent (considerably removed), her ideas of ablutionary performance were not to be appeased by a mere dab and douse. "Say nothing of the mess you make. Why can't you just *stand* in the tub even if you won't get down into it?

Way you do, whatever it is, you slop water all over the floor just when I 've got it scrubbed."

"Well," argued my father, "if you did n't set such tarnation store by this Sat'd'y-night washin' I would n't make no mess on the floor."

"But you *have* to be clean for Sunday," was her irrefutable contention. "You have clean bedclo'es on Sat'd'y night and you 'll have clean underclo'es in the morning." Wistfully adding, "You *want* to be clean for Sunday, don't you?"

"I wash my feet every night of my life — except mebbe sometimes in the winter — and I wash my face and neck every day. If you keep the bedclo'es clean and my clo'es clean, I can't be so very dirty, can I? You ought to have Ol' Covell to live with. I bet the' don't enough water touch him in a year to wet a worm."

"If I had Ol' Covell to live with," asserted my mother tartly, "I 'd *drown* him. Be the only way to get him clean, anyway."

"One thing you *can* make your mind up to," stated my father didactically, "is, I ain't goin' to get into no washtub on Sat'd'y night nor no other night. *You* can do what you like. And you can bring Delly up *in* a washtub if you want to. I won't interfere. But far 's I 'm concerned, I 've got along more 'n sixty years with such washin 's I see fit and I don't see no reason to change."

And change he did not. In hot weather he went nightly, as darkness came on to shield him, with a bar of soap and a towel to the bend in the river where the water was shallow. When the weather did not permit this natural attendance upon need, he got out a pail, filled it half full from the reservoir at the back of the stove, pulled his trouser legs up to his knees, and washed his feet and legs. I have seen him, too, after a shower or heavy dew, take off his shoes and stockings and go swishing through the grass back and forth to cool his tired feet. He doused his bald head in the basin, but he set no store on making a ceremony of this washing business as my mother did, and he was not impressed with any need for special measures in honor of the Sabbath.

As for the tub, he would have nothing to do with it. "Man 'd look pretty," he commented scornfully, "standin' there stark naked with his feet in a washtub! Could n't get no more of him in — can't even squat down in it. And I 'd ruther set down on the aidge of a chair and stick my feet in a pail than set perched up on the rim of a washtub any day."

"What you ought to have," Miz' Lou Esty told him conversationally, having overheard the weekly argument, "is one of these here contraptions like I saw to the Edwardses' in Jackson."

"What 's that?" my mother encouraged her.

"Well, they got a contraption they call a bathtub.

It's bigger 'n a washtub and kind of long and narrer, smaller 't one end 'n the other — looks somethin' like a coffin. They fill it with water and they can set right down into it."

My father, to the obvious surprise of his listeners, evinced unusual interest. He asked for more detailed description and finally remarked, "Well, if I *had* to get into any such tarnation contrivance, that might do. *I* don't know but I could make one." Many of the articles in our own home were of Father's construction, and my mother, with faith in his skill, rather encouraged such latent ambition until she learned from Miz' Esty that the thing was made of tin.

"It don't *hev* to be made of tin, does it?" argued my father. "The main thing, 's I see it, 's to make it big enough. If I'm goin' to hev to get into some kind of a tub to wash, I'm goin' to hev it so 's I can set down in it or not at all."

The first step in his creative effort was to haul an immense hogshead up out of the cellar through the hatchway, and saw it in two across the middle.

"What in time you doin' with that thing?" my mother demanded.

"I'm goin' to build me one of them tarnation bathtub things you been houndin' me about," he told her importantly, chalking and sawing.

"It'll fall apart," my mother said expertly, "soon 's it gets dried out."

"You hold your hosses," he advised her shortly. "It won't fall apart, not when *I* get through with it."

When the huge barrel was finally sawed and trimmed to his satisfaction, he took one half of it to the black-smith shop, where he had a couple of wagon tires welded about the top and another around the middle.

"Makin' a hoss troth?" inquired the smithy genially, to which Father only grunted in reply. He brought it home and showed it to my mother with an air of merited and expected approbation.

"There!" he exclaimed smugly. "Think *that* 'll fall apart? And I won't hev to lift water out of it, neither. I left the spigot into it on purpose. Just put a pail under — "

"You can't *get* a pail under," interrupted my mother, " 'thout you set it up on somethin', and then you could n't get up into it. You 'd have to have a ladder." Her tone, savoring of amusement rather than of proper com-mendation, did not please him.

"Well," he contended, "I can build a step up onto it — "

"And," continued his aggravating spouse, still lightly, "it 'll take more water 'n even the cistern holds to fill it."

"The 's the well, ain't the' — "

"And anyway, you could n't get it through the kitchen door."

Even this flagrant fact did not immediately disconcert

him. "Turn it over onto its side," he told her, but with diminishing confidence, "and it 'll roll through. I 'll show you."

Turn it any way he would, however, it would not roll in, nor could it be shoved, squeezed, or hoisted in.

"Well — " irritably he gave the offending device a kick which had no effect beyond injuring his most susceptible toe — "if you 'd a kept still about it in the first place, I would n't of had all this bother. You kept dingin' about it — "

"You fill it with dirt," my mother told him soothingly, "and I 'll plant portulacies in it. They 'll look real pretty trailin' over the aidge."

"Huh!" snorted my father, and ground his heel into the earth as he flung away. Later, the abortive attempt at modern bathing was hauled to the barnyard and made into a watering trough for the cattle, while my father followed his customary method of ablutions.

On Sunday morning, directly after the chores were done, he would take off his shirt and stand before the crazy rippling mirror over the wash bench to shave. First the razor had to be stropped by dexterously slapping it with vigorous strokes against an old red-brown strap of leather hanging on the wall. Then from the mug on which were lettered in gold the words "To Father" he would lather his face with a brush. With his razor he would scrape off the heavy bristle, and finally, taking the kitchen shears from their nail, he would trim his Greeley beard, and then subject his bald head to a merciless scrubbing. Lather flew; water splashed; he spluttered, blew like a porpoise, shook his head.

"Make more fuss and noise," my mother commented tolerantly, " 'n Old Mooley blowin' gnats out of her nose."

His toilet made, my father usually set the sails for the day's activities. In spring and summer there were certain customs amounting almost to obligations or pleasurable duty, whichever way you chose to look at it, that must be taken care of before other of the day's industries could be pursued. Such, for instance, as salting the sheep.

Now salting the sheep as a rite, ceremony, practice, employment, mission, or other agenda pertaining to the day's occupation was so richly fraught with adventure that, so far as I know either by experience or by hearsay, it is not equaled in all the diversions of the present week-end offered to sated man. This was particularly true on any one of the early spring Sabbaths bordering upon Paas Sunday, known to present haughty generations as Easter.

I do not know that I can claim any greater religious observance for that time than now — measured, that is, by spiritual fervor. But adjudged by the benefits of a tranquil and peaceful mind, an altogether satisfied estate, the custom of observing the Day of the Resurrection by salting the sheep is so infinitely superior to a promenade on the Mall as not to be mentioned in the same breath.

The sheep were kept in a pasture lot some considerable distance from the house and approached by way of a lane. And a lane, according to my acquaintance with such means of approach, is a private thoroughfare devoted to the peregrinations of cattle, mowers, reapers, and binders, rakes and other tools in transit from one field to another, to boys and dogs driving cattle, and to men and boys going fishing. In the early spring it is more of a locale of possibilities and promise than one of ful-fillment and discovery. On the south side of the log or stake-an'-rider fence that confines it, there may be, if the weather is forward, a few bunches of Paas blows, Easter blossoms, or windflowers, and the dogtooth violet, with a particularly precocious disposition, will stick an impudent tongue out from the greening sod. Almost of a certainty there will be dandelion greens at the edge of the stone pile, against which prospects we have fortified ourselves with basket and knife, carried by my father in one hand, in his other hand the tin pail containing salt, while Shep and I gambol at his side.

A little later, say about the time my father and I, with tamarack pole and tin of worms, take our sundown way along this same lane toward the meadow through which a little river runs, for a mess of bullheads — about this time the crooked fence of weather-seasoned rails will be a line of verdant and colorful charm. The wild morning-glory will put forth its pink bud; the thorny blackberry is mistily starred; there are elderberry bushes with flat thin cakes of furry bloom in one corner of the rundled fence and a clump of red-stemmed Old World elecampane in another. Edging the middle path which the cattle have trod are clover — low, sweet, fine-leaved clover with a greenish-white small bloom, honeyed food for bees. Young, robust spears of corn whisper from the field beyond one fence, with a waving sea of potential grain on the other side. Bobwhite calls plaintively from stubbled field, and fireflies flash their lanterns from the misty marsh. Later there will be abundant life to delight the eye, the nose, the ear. Just now, on this early Sabbath of spring, there is only the piping of frogs in the swale beyond the meadow, the trill of a song sparrow swaying from a reed, a red-winged blackbird's burst of melody from alder bush or osier. And from the bars beyond, the eager bleating of the sheep.

As I ride through the country nowadays my eye is caught by the gleaming white of the salt block that is put inside the pasture bars for cattle to lick at as they will. It is doubtless a more convenient method for the harried farmer, who must somehow steal time for radio, movies, and comic sheet, but recent communication with experts in the sheep-raising business tells me that the old method was better for the sheep.

And certainly the older custom was one means of

youthful education, the loss of which is sadly to be deplored. How is a child ever to know why a woodchuck has two holes instead of one, what becomes of the tails of tadpoles when they turn into frogs, and where turtles lay their eggs, if he never goes with his father to salt the sheep? How, in the name of the soul's advancement, is he ever to know where the brown thrush nests, or that mare's-tails in the sky are a threat of storm? What a sun dog is? Where the end of the rainbow lies? What a mackerel sky forebodes?

Churchgoing in that day was by no means an obligatory disposal of any part of the day, since the necessary harvesting of crops or the less virtuous custom of visiting among relations was occasionally allowed to intervene. Such forbearance, however, in no way indicated a lack of reverence. The spiritual life of the farmer of that time was pretty well a fixed quantity, however much the intelligence of its quality might be questioned by the materialist of to-day. He did not talk about it, or even think about it overmuch, but it had its feet pretty well set in a creed of decency, and whether he met his neighbors weekly in the little church at the Corners or not, he was one with them in Christian observance of the laws of humanity and what, to him, stood for brotherly love. Churchgoing was but one part of the outward and visible evidence of his simple rules for living.

Still, there was the Church, forming, if not a tenable backbone to the spiritual life of the community, at least an indication of its significance. We did not go to church to serve and worship God for an hour and then forget all about Him the rest of the week. We were taught the Ten Commandments and to abide by them. We were taught to honor our fathers and our mothers, and we did. We asked blessings, gave thanks, and said our prayers. We did not bear much false witness against our neighbor, but when he did not behave himself we either gave him a schoolin' or took him to law. We did not steal, we did not covet our neighbor's ox or his ass — and it wasn't overly safe to covet his wife. And we didn't commit adultery — often. Such "goin's-on" were frowned upon. We probably lived in fear of God, but I have still to see that a little wholesome fear is bad for either the soul or the deeds of man.

Then there was the social aspect of churchgoing. You tried to get there a bit early in order to have a brief visit with the neighbors before the services began, especially in summer. The men, after putting the horses in the shed or hitching them to the rail, congregated in the shade of surrounding trees to discuss crops and politics, although they were much more concerned with the former than with the latter, except in years of a "campaign" or some national calamity. The women gathered around the steps and talked about their children, their housework, each other. It did not so much matter what they talked *about* — as that there was opportunity to talk, to meet, to warm themselves at a communal fire.

If church was held in the morning it began early, about ten, and there was an "intermission" when folks went out into the churchyard to inspect the resting places of their dead. Myrtle grew thick over the graves and the little blue stars among the evergreen leaves seemed more appropriate to this peaceful spot than any flower I have seen there since.

Graves were not flattened down level with the earth in those days — such careless invitation to an inadvertent foot would have been considered base sacrilege. You would no more have stepped on the grave of the dead than on the hand of a prostrate man. Graves were lifted, rounded, sodded, marked at head and foot, sometimes with the tiny figure of a recumbent lamb for a little, loved child. And you walked reverently between the rows, reading from the mossy stones the names and dates and loving tributes to the dead. Nor did you gossip, laugh, or chatter to disturb the peace of that quiet spot. You trod gently, circumspectly, and you hushed your voice. And when church was over you went home to get dinner.

The provident housewife, of course, had her dinner well under way before going to church, and Sunday dinner had a few frills and furbelows in excess of the regular week-day dinner. On Easter Sunday, for instance,

there would be the chicken. Not that chicken (so-
called regardless of age) is any rarity to the farm home,
especially on a Sunday, but it seems to have an especial
appropriateness to Easter, as the turkey has to Thanksgiving. We always have had chicken on Easter, and
so long as we have a poultry yard we probably always
shall.

There will be chicken, then, with biscuits or dumplings.
Whichever form the mixture of flour and milk (sweet or
sour) may take, the result will be eminently satisfactory
— light as the down which was plucked from the breast
of the bird, and a competent absorbent for the gravy,
rich of flavor, smooth with yellow cream, and further
mellowed with butter.

Potatoes are getting a bit flabby with age, but crisped
overnight in cold water, cooked in plentifully salted water,
mashed and enriched with cream and butter, and finally
doomed to obscurity by an inundation of the delectable
gravy, they are to be borne. It will be a good five
months before we can get new potatoes, so we may as
well accept them — as we do — for what they are.

If the season has been a little advanced we shall have
the mess of dandelions gathered on our way to the sheep.
Young, tender, racy dandelions, just hinting of that
gusty bitterness which will increase in strength with the
season. Dandelions boiled with salt pork and dressed
with vinegar not too sharp, salt, and pepper.

Parsnips there may be, too. Parsnips dug from the

newly thawed earth, crisp and savory — for those who like parsnips. No farmer or gardener of that day would have dreamed of taking a parsnip from the earth in the fall of the year. There was a superstition to the effect that an unfrozen parsnip was poisonous. This belief has been exploded along with other credulities regarding foods, but the fact is that a parsnip is much improved in flavor by remaining in earth all winter, and is not injured by freezing.

Besides the parsnips, — preferably fried, — there will be onions boiled and dressed with butter and cream. Cream, you will note, played a generous part in the culinary preparations of that day. Cream and butter. Both were provided on the farm, neither had great commercial value, and so they were used in plenty. And to make any mention of the jellies, preserves, pickles, and relishes would be to read lavishly from the roster of cellar shelves.

For dessert — no strawberry shortcake for *that* Easter dinner, for the very good reason that there were no strawberries. We did not run to market and buy strawberries at thirty-five cents a pint in March or April. We waited until they ripened on our own vines all in their own good time, and were by that much better than any imported fruit that ever was, and the more enjoyed.

What we may have is Floating Island, scorned by my father as having no substance — "No better 'n soap bubbles to put your teeth into"; or syllabub, equally intangible; or tarts with raspberry jam — tarts baked in tiny fluted tins called "patty-pans." Or — once Miz' Lou Esty from her urban experiences had taught us the mystery of its concoction — ice cream. Made with rich milk, eggs, cornstarch, sugar, and more cream. Cooked as a custard and then frozen. Ice cream with frosted cake!

After dinner, and the day well on toward its peaceful end, there are any one of a dozen pleasant diversions, according to the season. My mother, on, say, a summer afternoon following the preparation of a Sunday dinner in the hot kitchen, with consequent dishes to wash, will probably sit in her old rocker on the front stoop to watch the fellows and their girls go riding by in the dusk, or to doze. She would not think of knitting or sewing on the Sabbath Day.

My father and I may go down to the river to get sweet flag to chew, or over to the swamp, where he will whittle a willow whistle and dig a hunk of gum from the bark of a tamarack tree. Or we may sit for an hour at the edge of the pond watching the turtles sunning themselves on a log, and listening to the various generations of frogs practising a harmony for the summer's overture, while Shep noses for muskrats along the bank.

After the chores are done, the milk strained and put away, chickens fed, wood box and chip pan filled, horses bedded, we have our frugal supper of bread and milk.

We yawn and look at the clock.   It has been a long day, and full.   In the short remaining hour before bedtime, one of the neighbors may drop in — Ol' Covell to borrow a go-devil for to-morrow's chopping ("tarnation slack old coot — never has any tools of his own"), or Lem Bouldry as Roadmaster, to discuss the division of labor.   Drowsily, at any rate, the hour will pass and the day is done.   We have remembered the Sabbath, and if we have not kept it holy according to some interpretations of Scriptural law, we have kept it according to our own honest code, and we have been satisfied with our way of doing it.   We go to sleep content, refreshed, strengthened, ready for the morrow.   We have no regrets, no great disappointments — and conversely no great exaltations of joy or excitement.   We have reached no heights, consequently we have no depths to plumb. We have had a peaceful, pleasant, profitable day, and we have remembered the Sabbath — in our hearts.

VI

The Strawberry Festival

THE Strawberry Festival was not so fixed an annual observance in our community as the Sunday School picnic,
for instance, but it was recognized as one of those social
affairs designed to further some worthy cause.

Upon one occasion which I remember as well for the
calamity that nearly befell as for the luscious feast that
it was, the actuating need was a suddenly disclosed but
apparently overwhelming demand for new hymnbooks for
the church. Miz' Lou Esty, whenever she went to the
city to sew for her more fashionable patrons, invariably
brought back some innovations for our improvement. She
it was who introduced the stylish method of placing the
twirled napkin in our goblets, and it was she again who
came home from one of these urban visits filled with zeal
for a more modern version of tuneful praise than was
afforded by the old hymnbooks. She was a considerable
leader in all church affairs, including the choir, where
her somewhat nasal soprano soared stridently above all
other voices, and if Miz' Esty found the old hymnbooks
wanting, there were none to argue. All the town churches,

she said, had new hymnbooks with brighter, livelier tunes than the old ones, and less morbid words.

"You take that one now," she was telling my mother one evening in late May, as they did the dishes together in our kitchen, "about 'Hark, from the tomb a doleful sound.' That ain't no kind of a tune to sing where there's children."

Miz' Esty had no real home of her own except a room over at Bouldrys', where, as she sometimes said, she went between threading one needle and another. She was a sociable body, however, and did n't favor staying long in her one room, so she often came to our house to stay a few days at a time. The most of her sewing for country families was done in February and March before women got too busy with house cleaning, gardening, and chickens, so here she was now, telling us about the new hymnbooks folks were buying in town. My mother, ever alert for signs of progress in the outside world, agreed with her.

"I never thought it was any kind of a hymn for any-body," she said, wringing out her dishcloth and hanging it to dry behind the stove. "What kind of tunes has this new hymnbook got?"

"Well, there's one that goes — " Miz' Lou Esty, the ends of a linen dish towel held in her two hands like a baton, broke into a rather shrill treble, keeping time with nodding head, rhythmic towel, and the faintest suggestion of swaying hips: —

"B-*ring*-ing in the sheaves,
B-*ring*-ing in the sheaves,
We shall come re-*joic*-ing
B-*ring*-ing in the sheaves."

My mother stood at respectful and admiring attention, her hands folded lightly across the full gathers of her
apron.

"My!" she said, as Miz' Esty concluded her performance and the glow of ecstasy faded from her face. "That
is nice. I'd like to hear the whole of it."

My father, his paper lowered, head bent that he might
peer over his steel-rimmed glasses, grunted.

"Don't you like it, Mr. Thompson?" asked Miz' Esty
unwisely. She never did learn that the better part of wisdom, in dealing with my father, was not to question him
unless you wanted bitter truth.

"Good enough song," he replied gruffly, "if you're
tryin' to beat a thunderstorm in harvestin'. Can't see
what it's got to do with *religion*, though."

"Why, that's plain," Miz' Esty told him fatuously.
"It just means if you're *good*, why — why — "

My father snorted and raised his paper. "When you
get a new hymnbook," he told her shortly, "that'll beat
'Rock of Ages,' you let me know."

Nevertheless, Miz' Esty found a sufficient number of
adherents to further her plan, and the church voted to
buy new hymnbooks. The next thing was to get the

money with which to buy them. The Strawberry Festival was the final plan, and this was also Miz' Esty's idea.

"I told 'em," she reported at our house as we sat at supper on the evening after the meeting of the Ladies' Aid where the decision was made, " 't I knew Mr. Thompson 'd donate the berries. You'd do that, would n't you, Mr. Thompson?"

Two things, among a considerable number of others my father hated, were familiarity or any imposition upon his dignity, and having someone else make promises for him. Few people who knew him ever ventured either trespass, but Miz' Esty, although doubtless talented as a costumer, was a little weak in her perceptions. She now waited in smiling confidence as my father fidgeted with his knife and fork, spilled his tea, and grew dark of brow. My mother watched him with knowing apprehension.

"Wa-a-l," he drawled finally, "if I 'd a — been *asked* about it, I 'd a — prob'ly looked into it."

"My goodness!" exploded Miz' Esty. "I *told* you about it. They want to get new hymnbooks."

"Yes," said my father, helping himself elaborately to a second supply of cold dandelion greens and fried potatoes, "I heard tell they did — some of 'em."

"Well!" Miz' Esty's voice registered both impatience and indignation. "The Ladies' *Aid* decided on it. And we all thought you 'd donate the berries. You 're always givin' away berries."

"Yes," said my father, liberally spreading freshly churned butter on freshly baked bread, "that's one reason I grow 'em. To give 'em away — when I want to."

Always there came a certain point in the domestic relations of our family when my mother's tolerant understanding and tactful handling would bring at least a cessation of argument.

"Why, yes," she now intervened, "we're always glad to share our berries — what we don't sell — if we have plenty. How does the berry crop look, 'Lijer?" Thus did she divert his attention from hymns to horticulture.

"Well," said my father, pushing his chair back from the table and brushing a crumb from his vest, "they flowered good. If we don't have a frost — but strawberries is about the reskiest crop the' is . . ." And the contract for donating strawberries for the Festival, while not enthusiastically given, was, nevertheless, tacitly assured. The weather was all that could be desired; the crop promised abundance. Preparations for the Festival proceeded, with no threat of halt in the performance until a committee of ladies came to our house one day in June to discuss the form of refreshments. The decision was retailed to my father at the conclusion of the evening meal.

"You mean to tell *me*," he shouted, turning on my mother, who was clearing the table, "that they're goin' to put them berries into *pies?*"

"Why, yes." Even my mother, who was used to his

outbursts, — quite harmless except in ferocity of tone, — was surprised at the violence of his manner. "Strawberries make a *good* pie — if you make it right."

"Strawberries ain't *meant* for pie! What in the name of *Tophet 's* the sense of spoiling *strawberries* puttin' 'em into a *pie?*"

"Well," expostulated my mother a little worriedly, "I s'pose they 've got a right to put the strawberries into pies if they want to. They thought it 'd be a change."

"Not *my* strawberries, they ain't! Why, 'Miry," he took a step toward her that by a stranger might have been interpreted as threatening. To my mother and me — a little girl dressing a Maltese cat in hood and mittens — he was just Pa, making a fuss about something to eat. "Why, Miry, it 'd be a *crime* to put the only kind of fruit on earth that 's fit for a shortcake into a pie that almost anything can be put into."

"You would n't think," said my mother dryly, continuing now with her supper work, "that you could put almost anything into a pie, the fuss you make about apple and punkin — and mince."

"Well," his voice dropped to a less heated tone as he pushed a chair against the wall with his foot, turned and paced the floor, his hands thrust severely into his overalls' pockets, "you *can* make a pie out of a lot of things, and you can't make a shortcake out of *anything* but strawberries."

"Oh, shaw! You can too!" My mother shut the

pantry door with conviction, and poured hot water over the dishes from the teakettle. "I 've made shortcake out of raspberries myself, and you 've eaten it."

"Yes, and you know what I thought about it, too. And anyway, them women won't get no strawberries out of me unless they put 'em into shortcake, way they ought to."

"Mebbe they would n't make *good* shortcakes if they did."

"Can't you make 'em yourself?"

"I can, but I won't," stated my mother firmly. "Not and give the berries too."

"*I 'd* give the berries and welcome," offered my father wistfully, "if you 'd make the shortcakes."

"I 'll make you all the shortcakes you want," she promised him faithfully, "till strawberries is over — but you 'll have to stand what you get to this Festival or stay to home."

He did not threaten to stay at home, but the uncertainty of what he might do resulted, by some diplomatic manœuvre on the part of my mother, in getting the *pièce de résistance* of the menu changed from pie to shortcake. He merely grumbled.

All, then, went well to the festive day. The church lawn was mowed, its edges trimmed with sickle and shears. Rows of lanterns swung gayly from one post to another. Tables, improvised from planks and "horses," were set up and clothed. Bouquets of red and white clover ornamented the centre line. My father picked the berries — cream of the crop — in the coolness of early morning and put them in the cellar. He gloated over them as he bore great basins of them through the kitchen.

"Berries like them," he boasted to my mother, holding a pan of huge crimson fragrant fruit under her nose, "ought to buy a tarnation good hymnbook." He chuckled. "Ought to have something in it about bringin' in the *berries,* 'stead of sheaves."

The Festival was to be held at six o'clock; and on a June day, in the height of strawberry season, at six o'clock the sun is still lambent, though the shadows lie long upon the grass.

Now a Strawberry Festival was at least an event of sufficient social importance to warrant new summer dresses, and perhaps a new straw hat. Men came in early from the fields and shaved. Some of the young men even stripped and bathed, though it was only the middle of the week — especially those who were going to take a girl. A visit to the barber on the Saturday night previous had resulted in hair cut and pomaded. Buggies had been washed, harness oiled and shined, horses curried and brushed.

Since we were to bring the berries with us, to be applied to the hot shortcake at the last moment, we went a bit early, my father demurring but little at the waste of time and what to him seemed a foolish custom of eating out of doors.

"Worst time in the whole year to eat outdoors," he grumbled. "Gnats and skeeters — "

"Too early for skeeters," my mother encouraged him, as she brushed his alpaca coat and worn breeches, "and it's too high for gnats. Gnats stay on low land. Now for heaven's sake don't forget the berries. The ones for the shortcakes is in a stone crock and the others in a basket with grape leaves over 'em." For it had been decided that not only should there be shortcake, but strawberries and cream to follow.

"Foolishest thing I ever heard of," declared my father truculently, "spoilin' two o' the best dishes in the world, crowdin' 'em." But nevertheless he had scoured his vines to find the largest, ripest, finest berries for the latter dish, exulting in their fragrance and beauty.

He went to get the horse and buggy, I with him, while my mother took a last look around the house.

We arrived upon a gay and festive scene. Men dawdled upon and around the steps of the church. Boys and girls walked in the graveyard, white dresses catching on the filmy fingers of pale green eglantine that grew by the gate, clumsy, tender hands releasing. Women gathered about the table. Everybody, it would seem, was there, except the Covells. "Land's sakes!" commented my mother as we drove up. "What's happened to the Covells? They're gen'r'lly the first!"

Miz' Simpson, living nearest the church, had volun-
teered to make the shortcakes and arrived at the same
moment as we did.

"You bring along the berries, 'Lije," commanded my
mother, hurrying off to the table. "Take Delly with
you."

So my father and I drove to the hitching rack and
left the horse. Then, with the gray stone jar held carefully in one arm, the basket of whole berries in the
other, he led the way back through smiling, welcoming
groups to the improvised worktable where my mother was
impatiently waiting.

Miz' Simpson was removing the towels from the
shortcakes, Miz' Bouldry was lavishly spreading the
steaming halves with butter. My mother grabbed the
heavy stone jar from my father's hands, set it on
the table, and snatched off the cover. Her head and neck
gave a convulsive jerk as she leaned over the crock.
She bent farther over, the better to peer. A look of
utter dismay overspread her face. She leaned heavily
with her hands upon the table, and slowly lifted a pal-
lid, horrified face to my father. The people around her
were frozen with apprehension. My father stared at her.

"Lard!" she whispered. *"Lard!* You got the wrong
crock!" My father took a step forward and glared
unbelievingly into the jar.

"I got it where you told me," he said nervously, "on
the cellar shelf."

My mother threw both hands to her head, knocking the hat that sat precariously on her mop of black hair to a rakish angle.

"*Oh, Lord!*" she breathed, not unpiously. "I brought 'em up to sweeten and forgot."

My father fell back, shocked and silent. No word was spoken. Alarm and consternation had spread from group to group. Without their knowing the depth of catastrophe, its shadow had fallen. Nothing, it seemed, could redeem the situation.

Our house, our kitchen, and the jar of berries in it, were two miles away. The shortcakes were cooling; the butter, in spite of the slanting rays of a June sun, was stiffening. The berries, the crimson luscious berries with their sweet juice, were far away. Sheridan with his mere twenty miles and a good fast horse to cover the distance was as a wraith of mist before the wind compared to those two miles and a spoiling crust.

Then Miz' Bouldry came to life. "Well, my land!" she exclaimed confidently. "It ain't as if we did n't *have* berries. We 'll just use these." She was stripping the leaves from the basket, to my father's indignant dismay, when, with a clatter of hoofs and a rattle of loosened spokes, the Covells hove into view.

The Covells were certain to be counted on where food was plentiful and good, regardless of cost. They were too poor to buy the children decent clothes, but never too poor to pay for a church supper. Never before had they been known to be late, and on the way over my father had made some caustic speculation as to whether the Covells would already be seated at the tables, tongues a-droolin'.

But here they came, Ol' Covell "g'langing" at the lean team that drew them, the girls flopping and banging about on the two improvised board seats across the box of the wagon, Mrs. Covell waving one hand violently in the air and hanging for dear life with the other — to a stone crock in her lap!

Every eye was lifted to their approach. My father stood open-mouthed, his old sweat-stained straw hat pushed back on his bald head. My mother, pale and stricken, seemed hardly to sense the agitation.

"Hey!" shouted Miz' Covell as the team drew up with a lurching flourish. "Lookit! We got the berries!"

My mother gasped. My father lunged forward, strode, grabbed the jar from Miz' Covell's astonished hands, and plunked it down on the table.

"There!" he said, with the air of a man who has accomplished miracles, but not unwittingly.

It appeared, when anyone was sufficiently recovered from shock to listen, that Miz' Covell had been asked to contribute sugar to the Festival (as a preventive measure against having to eat any of her cooking), and, finding herself short, — a customary condition of her larder, — had stopped to borrow of my mother.

Opening the unlocked door, she had helped herself to the sugar, and then, led by her nose, had found the stone jar of fragrant fruit. Suspecting the situation, she had snatched up the crock and egged her astonished spouse — accustomed to moderation in all personal activity — to speed, and here they were.

My mother bent happily to the belated inundation of flaky crust with crimson berries; my father swaggered a little from group to group, showing his basket of tempting fruit.

"Best crop I ever had," he said. "Why, *five* of them berries 'll fill a cup." No one thought to question the size of the cup.

Miz' Lou Esty's voice clarioned. Long pantalooned legs slid over the rude benches at the side of the table. Modestly garmented ankles slipped in beside them. Hats were recklessly flung upon the grass. The Committee "waited." Young men properly attended their ladies, as did older men — when they remembered.

The menu was simple, but plenteous, since this was a supper rather than the usual Festival fare of berries, ice cream, and cake. It consisted of a dish announced by Miz' Esty as Chicken Cheese — another urban innovation the rule for which she had brought back with her from the Edwardses — and instantly denounced by my father when she had discussed it with my mother at the outset of plans.

"Why in *tunket* they want to chonk up their chicken

beforehand?" he wanted to know. "Cold fried chicken 's good enough for *any*body."

"We *always* have fried chicken," declared my mother in defense of Miz' Esty's argument. "Seems good to have a change."

My father snorted. *"Change!"* he barked. "What 's the sense in changing anything that 's good the way it is?"

In this, however, probably because she had stood in favor of shortcake as against pie, my mother arrayed herself with Miz' Esty and her "Chicken Cheese."

It was a tasty dish, as I recall it, and the rule which I find in one of my old cookbooks sounds not unappetizing, although by and large I agree with my father as to the merits of fried chicken on, as you might say, the hoof.

To make Chicken Cheese you "take a chicken and cook it very tender. Cook the gravy or liquor of the chicken down to a jell. Take out all the bones and chop the meat; season with salt, pepper, and a little sage. Put it then into a mould and pour the liquor over it. When cold, take out and slice."

My own translation of this recipe as rendered in later days calls for one small onion finely chopped and a seasoning of celery salt in addition. I also use a tablespoonful of dissolved gelatin to a pint of the strong liquor to pour over the meat. And I garnish it with hard-boiled egg sliced, radish roses, and parsley. It differs from the original recipe only in being more highly seasoned and dressed up a little.

There were scalloped potatoes, hot and smoking, the top of each tin basin encrusted with an amber film shading to brown and bisque, oozing, at a touch, a creamy liquid rich with the salty zest of butter.

There were riz biscuits, differing pleasantly from the baking-powder consistency of the shortcakes, and there was a huge bowl of young lettuce leaves dressed with mild vinegar, sugar, and salt, and served on saucers. There were tart cucumber pickles and dill pickles, but the generous impulse of some to contribute preserves and other sweets had been restrained. "You don't want sweet things," my mother had told them, "just before you eat shortcake. Spoil the taste of it if you do."

And the shortcake! With all due allowance made for the lapse of time between the uncovering of Miz' Simpson's cakes and the arrival of the berries for their rosy thatch, there could not have been much wrong, it seems to me, with that shortcake, judging by the manner in which it disappeared. And yet, on our way home, my father acidly remarked that so far as he was concerned they might just as well have kept their shortcake to home. The *berries* was all right, but it was a pity to waste 'em on a shortcake like that.

"Why, 'Lije," differed my mother, "that was good shortcake; it wasn't made with sour milk the way I do, that's all."

"Well," he grumbled as we jogged homeward, "we'll

have to wait couple days now 'fore we can have *any* shortcake." Then he chuckled rumblingly into his stubby beard. "Had n't been for them danged snoopin' Covells," he muttered, "we might a had *plenty* shortcake to-morrow."

For the rule by which my mother made her sour-milk shortcake — or one similar to it — I have had to search through such old "receipt books" as are treasured by the daughters of her contemporaries, since she left no record of her own. What I have found contains all the ingredients, and in proper proportions, as nearly as we can judge. Of course I am giving you modern, level measurements where the old books call for "heaping" teaspoonfuls and "cups" of this and that, heaven only knowing what size the cups were. But here it is, according to our translation, and you must do the best you can with it. For by what necromancy my mother welded these ingredients together I do not know, but try as I may I cannot persuade my palate that a shortcake made to-day, using exactly the same component parts, tastes *quite* as did those so inextricably mingled in memory with the rare, sweet Junes of my childhood. Perhaps it was the berries — my father was a master hand at raising berries. None nowadays taste nearly so sweet or have such *strawberry* flavor. Perhaps it was the butter. There *is* no such butter now as that which enriched

— both outside and in — my mother's shortcake. Perhaps it was because my father said it was good — for when my father said a thing was good you could take his word for it. It *was* good. And — perhaps it was because my mother made it!

At any rate, here are the things she put in it, and, so far as I can tell, the way she put them together (according to this old dog-eared book lent me by the daughter of the first owner, who cooked by practically the same rules). And I can only hope that you will have the skill (or luck) to bring forth something that will give you half the epicurean pleasure that my mother's shortcakes gave us.

To two cups of flour take one teaspoonful of baking soda, one teaspoonful of salt, four tablespoonfuls of shortening (half butter), and about a cup and a half of sour milk, "lobbered." Sift the flour, salt, and soda together into a bowl, and work in the shortening. Make a hole in the centre and pour in the milk, stirring the flour into it from the sides with a wooden spoon. The dough should be just as soft as it can be handled, so the amount of milk is indefinite. Pour it out on to a floured board and then pat it out or roll it gently — handling it just as little as possible — to a cake about three quarters of an inch thick. Put this into a buttered baking tin either square or oblong and bake it in a hot oven (450 degrees) for fifteen minutes.

The amount of soda depends somewhat on the sourness of the milk. Do not try to sour pasteurized milk, for it cannot be done. It will get "old" but it will not "lobber." And if you don't know what "lobbered" means, it means thick — the dictionary stylishly calls it "clabbered." If you use too much soda, the cake will be yellow and taste like lye. Of course you may be safer in making a baking-powder dough, in which case you take your regular recipe for biscuits but add another tablespoonful of shortening (using half butter, at least, for the shortening) and bake it the same way.

When your cake is done (and "shortcake" in my kind of recipe does n't mean "biscuits"), proceed after this fashion: have your strawberries (dead ripe) washed, hulled, mashed, and sweetened, in a bowl (my mother used a blue bowl and I am reasonably sure it was Staffordshire, but it was not prized and she used it because the berries looked so pretty in it). And be sure there are plenty of them.

Turn your hot cake out on a platter and split it in two, laying the top half aside while you give your undivided attention to the lower. Spread this most generously with butter just softened enough (but never melted) to spread nicely, and be sure to lay it on clear up to the very eaves. Now slosh your berries on, spoonful after spoonful — all it will take. Over this put the top layer, and give it the same treatment, butter and berries, and let them drool off the edges — a rich, red, luscious, slowly oozing cascade of ambrosia. On the top place a few whole berries — if you want to — and get it to the table as quickly as you can. It should be eaten just off the warm, and if anybody wants to deluge it with cream, let him do so. But the *memory* of a strawberry short-cake like this lies with the cake and not with cream.

VII

An Apple a Day — and More

THE apple orchard was as much an accepted corollary
of the farm of Southern Michigan as the cornfield or
meadow. Farmers in our particular locality did not
depend much upon the apple crop as a commercial enterprise, but rather as one of the natural contributions to
the larder. And although there was plenty of every
kind of fruit indigenous to this part of the country, such
as pears, peaches, plums, and the smaller fruits, it was
the apple upon which we most depended, because it had
the longest season, survived the most diversified usage,
and was, all in all, the stay upon which we leaned for
fruit variance in our diet.

My mother, whose mind sometimes took a fanciful
turn for all her practicality, loved the orchard from the
first red bud which showed among the young green
leaves to the last frostbitten fruit falling from its rimed
branch, and was much diverted by the mellifluous and
sometimes romantic names by which they were known.
My father, being somewhat of a gourmet, found more

pleasure in contemplating the aromatic odor of an **Early Harvest** as suitable for a green-apple pie.

I, too, hold in treasured memory the rich lusciousness of that queen of desserts, but partake sufficiently of my mother's more poetic nature to find myself remembering the fragrant sweetness of the bridal bloom and, later, the rich, heady odor of ripening fruit; remembering hours of childish leisure passed in savoring one ambrosial offering after another, lying full length upon the grass where windfalls spent their wasted opulence, or harbored in some accommodating crotch, where unerasable pictures of orchard beauty were imprinted on my mind.

The Early Harvest was the first to lend spice and variety both as "sauce" for the table and as green-apple pie. Now, a green-apple pie, along in summer after you had had your fill of custards because eggs were plentiful, and especially if yours was the kind of cuisine where dried apples filled in that dismal period between the last of the Baldwins or Russets and the first of the Early Harvests, was a matter for praise and benediction. But it is so long since I have set my yearning teeth into a green-apple pie such as was known to my youth that I falter before contemplation of even the memory lest I be overcome with nostalgia. To buy green apples from the market and blend them, although by measurement and rule, with spices and sugar, flour and shortening, is but to court vast discontent. The apples lack in crispness and in flavor. The shortening does not come out of a crock in the cellar. The flour is ground from wheat grown God knows where. The whole is combined in a state of doubt and by a hand lacking the skill acquired in loving service. What, alas, can be expected from such a dubious beginning?

The Early Harvest tree was found in every orchard large or small. The fruit was yellow — not a thick speckled yellow like the Punkin Russet, for instance, but clear and pale, almost transparent. The flesh was juicy and tender. The green fruit was quite tart, as was proper for pies, but as it ripened it became better for eating than for cooking.

Following closely upon the Early Harvest came the Red Astrachan, a gentle and beautifully cultured daughter of Pomona flaunting gypsy dress — a Roman veil of crimson stripes over a yellow slip, all misted in bluish bloom. A midsummer apple, juicy, tender, excellent for sauce or eating.

Then there was the Seek-No-Further — an apple lovely as its name. It is many years since I have even seen a Seek-No-Further tree. But I well remember the way it grew — a well-rounded, low-boughed tree, sturdy and vigorous. And although I have no recollection of having seen or tasted the fruit in an equal number of years, and do not even know whether it is still grown in Southern Michigan, I can visualize the apple perfectly — roundish in form, with a somewhat tough skin, greenish yellow in color, wearing a top skirt of bright red which, when rubbed against your sleeve or skirt, took on a fine bright polish. When you bit into it the meat was just a little yellow, but nice and crisp, breaking off in neat chunks with a fine crunch to them, juicy and tart.

But the Seek-No-Further was only one in an opulent roster of names that enrich the memory of one whose early days were blessed, amid a wealth of country sights, sounds, odors, and tastes, with the living friendliness of an orchard.

By late September the different varieties of early fall apples were coming on. One that I remember with keenest pleasure was what we called the "Greasy Pippin." There is, it seems, quite a large Pippin family — the word meaning a "pip" or seed. A Pippin, then, originally meant a seedling, and there are, by name, the Newton Pippin, the Fall Pippin, the Missouri Pippin, and innumerable other progeny. Nowhere, however, can I find reference to any of such questionable origin as one might suspect from the descriptive term of Greasy Pippin, and I am told that another colloquial name for it was the Tallow Pippin, known also in New York State as Lowell.

This was, at any rate, quite a good-sized apple, with a skin thin but tough (with teeth and tongue you could do a pretty thorough job of skinning), pale greenish yellow in color. And the skin was decidedly greasy —

although I suppose the horticulturist would refer to it as "waxy" — to the touch.

The flesh was yellowish, tender, and very juicy, and made excellent sauce and grand pie before the fruit got too ripe. The apple bruised easily and when very ripe fell to the ground with a wet sort of plop — and squshed. When buckwheat was planted in the orchard and the apples fell upon the stubble, there they would lie, pierced to the core, their honeyed juices exuding for the delectation of wasps and bees.

Another favorite of those days — but whether for actual flavor or because of its name I do not know — was the Maiden Blush, which ripened in September. This was a handsome apple, clad in a mantle of creamy yellow, with, as one would expect, a fine healthy crimson flush on the cheek. It was good for cooking but not for keeping. Housewives favored it for drying, since the flesh was tender and juicy.

I am inclined to pass over the entire subject of drying — and dried — apples with the same tactful disregard which I have sometimes shown to other uninspiring subjects — as, for instance, tripe. Still, the housewives of my childhood's day did dry apples. Even my own mother, who had a high regard for the flavor and excellence of all food, stooped to that ignoble economy. For hour after hour, which, to my father's mind and mine, might have been spent in any one of a dozen more profitable ways, she would sit and peel, quarter, and core apples for drying. Perfectly good apples that might better have been eaten fresh, as they stood, and then remembered for what they were.

But no. Peeled they must be, cored, quartered, and flung into cold water. Not for the sake of cleanliness, I think, for what was a little unnecessary laving now on apples fresh from the impregnable protection of skin, as against the days of slow dehydration in a hazardous exposure to dust — and worse.

But washed they were, and then strung by darning needle and cord into long dangling ropes which were hung over the stove, behind the stove, out of doors, wherever they would dry; or laid on racks in the sun and covered with mosquito netting as perfunctory protection against the marauding fly, the zealous wasp — but utterly inadequate to withstand dust or the more insinuating encroachment of midges, gnats, and mites. When, finally, the shrunken sections resembled nothing so much as a bit of chewed, spewed, and dried sole leather, they were stripped from the cord, stored in cloth bags, and slung to nails in the garret against that unhappy day when the last apple in the bin, the last in the apple hole outside, was gone, and a withered, insipid, soulless substitute must take its place.

Stewed, as in sauce, this unsavory impostor was sometimes bolstered up by a slice of lemon in an attempt to delude the hankering appetite, but in vain.

My father hated dried apples — as all right-minded people should — and would have no part in their preparation. Moreover, he disliked seeing my mother spend pleasant hours in what he called a wicked waste, cutting up perfectly good apples to make something that, he declared, a hog would n't eat.

"But," contended my mother, "we can't use the apples now — and they won't keep. Come spring, we shan't have any. Ain't dried apples better 'n none?"

"No," replied my father promptly, "not by a jugful. *Nothin's* better 'n a dried apple." A statement literally meant.

One day while the orgy of apple drying was at its height, my father came home from town bringing a supposedly time-saving contrivance which you fastened to the edge of the table, and on a fork of which was impaled an apple. Then you turned a crank and a projecting knife did the peeling. He amused himself for a while experimenting with the thing and to his surprise found that it worked better than he expected. Barring a few instances, as when the apple split and went on the floor, or when he managed to cut his finger on the blade, the contraption seemed to go very well and he was quite pleased with himself for the discovery. Not content, however, with a reasonable success, he must try it on turnips and potatoes. The blade skipped and jumped.

Attempting to hold the object under abuse by main strength, he dislodged the machine from the table. It fell to the floor, striking a slightly bunioned joint, and was promptly kicked across the room.

"Tarnation fool thing!" he exploded, and laid the blame, as usual, on my mother. "If you was n't everlastingly tryin' to do what the neighbors do," he thundered, "I would n't of got it. Dryin' apples because Miz' Bouldry does!"

My mother took up her pan and knife and proceeded to peel, quarter, and core her apples, after the usual custom. "I 've dried apples," she said tranquilly, "ever since before Miz' Bouldry moved into the neighborhood. And I 've peeled 'em with a knife and I 'm goin' to keep on."

But lack of enthusiasm for dried apples, however, finally convinced my mother of the futility of her effort, especially when my father declared that he would rather have a "nerly old frozen apple 't had laid under the snow till spring 'n a dried apple any day."

That the attitude of my immediate family toward the dried apple and all its various ramifications is by no means an unusual one is attested by the corroboration of many others. That, on the other hand, the dried apple has its loyal adherents is undeniably demonstrated by the measure of reproof with which my own disparaging convictions have been met. I have been accused of not giving the dried apple fair treatment, especially in not even mentioning several ways in which it shows up to best advantage. One of these, I am told, is in the concoction of a dish known as "Schnitz un Knepp" — a Pennsylvania dish. To make this delicacy, we are told that a quart of dried apples to three and a half pounds of ham is about the right proportion. The ham should be home-cured, and, of course, the apples home-dried, a combination which should not be difficult, since anyone who has a quart of home-dried apples on hand would be almost certain to be possessed also of three pounds of home-cured ham.

We are admonished to wash the apples — a caution strictly to be observed if they have been dried according to the customs with which I am familiar. They are then put in water, to cover, and allowed to soak overnight.

On the following morning the ham is put to cook in cold water and boiled for three hours. You then add the soaked apples, with the water in which they have been soaked, and boil for an hour longer. Add two tablespoonfuls of brown sugar and a little pepper. Now you make some dumplings by sifting together two cups of flour, four teaspoonfuls of baking powder, a teaspoonful of salt, a quarter teaspoonful of pepper; mix with three tablespoonfuls of melted butter and one well-beaten egg, and enough sweet milk to make a thick batter. Drop this in small spoonfuls into the hot apple and ham liquid, cover, and cook for fifteen or twenty minutes —

until the dumplings are done. It is served all together on a platter.

Now, there you are! *Schnitz un Knepp.* And that it doubtless deserves a place among the apple favorites of all time is evidenced by the fact that it has been found worthy of the poet's art: —

I am a man well up in years with simple tastes and few,
But I would like to eat again a dish my boyhood knew.
A rare old dish that Mother made that filled us all with pep,
This generation knows it not — we called it *Schnitz and Knepp.*
I patronize all restaurants where grub is kept for sale,
But my search up to the present has been without avail.
They say they never heard of it, and I vainly wonder why,
For that glorious concoction was better far than pie.
Dried apple *snits*, a slab of ham and mammoth balls of dough
Were the appetizing units that filled us with a glow,
When Mother placed the smoking dish upon the dinner table,
And we partook of its delight as long as we were able.
My longing for that boyhood dish I simply will not shelf;
If I cannot find it anywhere, I'll make the thing myself.[1]

A most laudable resolution. But what is one to do when neither home-dried apples nor home-cured ham is available? As for me, I shall fry the ham and cook thick-sliced fresh apples and onions together. Or scallop some sweet potatoes and tart apples, generously potted with butter.

Trusting that the above contribution to the culinary value of the dried apple will be accepted as a sop to justice, we will return to the orchard from which, in its prime

[1] H. Luther Frees, in the *Pennsylvania Dutch Cookbook.*

and glory, it sprang, with, as my final apostrophe to its
be-sapped stepchild, this refrain: —

> Tread on my toes, and tell me lies,
> But *don't* give me dried-apple pies!

The sweet apples that came along in late summer
and fall have a decidedly fragrant place in the orchard
of my memory. Sweet Bough was the earliest of these.
That was the tree that grew nearest the house, and
when the apples were fully ripe you would sometimes
hear them dropping in the night. It would be in the
first hour before sleep, when all was still, so you could
hear the guttural drumming of old Jug-o'-Rum down
on the riverbank and a forehanded cricket feebly pre-
dicting an early fall. And then, all of a sudden — ker-
plop! And you knew another Sweet Bough had grown
too heavy for its parent stem — honeyed food for ants
and bees.

Then there were Pound Sweets — better baked than
raw — and the Tolman Sweet, latest of all and cherished
for its excellent amalgamating qualities, being of a
temper that harmonized well with quince, the combination proving to be one of the favorite preserves for
our table.

Bellflower, Gillyflower — ah, the old Black Gillyflower,
an apple that may be, for all I know, entirely extinct.
A strange and foreign-looking fruit, conical in shape and
with a deeply indented and wrinkled nose, and rather

dry, the flesh growing mealy as it ripened.   But a handsome fruit withal — purple rather than black, an effect
gained by a wash of deep red over green, and a dark
blue bloom.

Greenings, Russets, Jonathans, Rambos, Snow.   Time
was when I thought the Snow apple as once grown in
Southern Michigan was unexcelled as an eating apple
except by what seemed to us then the queen of all apples, the Northern Spy.   We could hardly wait for the
Snow apple to ripen, so beautiful it was to gather — a
rich red skin with pure white flesh often veined with
crimson threads.   A tender, juicy, delicious apple it was,
but not much good for cooking.   Certainly the Snow
apple was one of the Michigan orchard's favorites of
that day, and yet I do not find it listed as "Snow Apple"
at all, but as only one of a great variety under the general family name of Fameuse.   I think even then farmers sometimes called it "Famous."

Greenings, Spitzenbergs, Winesaps, Wealthy, King,
Strawberry, and Baldwins were the late fall and winter
apples, the first two lasting until late winter and good
for both cooking and eating; the last, then as now, the
staple for keeping qualities.   The others were excellent
while they lasted, but not good keepers.

Early winter apples were stored in bins or barrels in
the cellar, but, at least by my father, the late winter
apples were buried in an "apple hole" outside, as were
some vegetables.   The pit was dug near the house,

where the ground was mellow, and lined with straw.
Then the apples were put in, covered with straw and
earth, and finally with the blanket of snow that was the
best protection of all. Along late in winter you went out
and dug away the snow and frozen earth, clawed down
into the straw, and brought out fresh, cold apples, crisp
and luscious.

Take a pan of these of a raw March evening along
with a plate of friedcakes, and sit down by the stove,
— maybe with a game of pitch or euchre when the neighbors drop in, — and who could ask for more?

This memory list of our most staple fruit is by no
means complete, and especially would it not be so without at least honorable mention of the crab apple.

The crab apple, however, did not usually have a place
in the orchard, but was set, rightfully and with due artistic taste, near the house, where, because of its gracious
rounded growth, it afforded gentle shade, and also a
wealth of beauty and odor during bloom. No sweeter,
more entrancing, ardent, and alluring fragrance sweet-
ens the summer air than that from the crab-apple bloom.
Nor is any sight lovelier than the pale sunset glow which
veils the snowy vestments clothing every branch and
limb. Unless, that is, it be the same tree in its rich
fulfillment — laden with tiny spheres of crimson and gold.
Above all, we must not forget its final contribution to
man's delight: those countless glasses of pellucid jelly

in varying shades of amber, rose, and claret that graced the storeroom shelves.

I aim to tell of certain apple dishes that came out of that old bee-laden, fragrant orchard, dishes that even a modern cook might concoct, but I despair of bringing before you with clarity of word sufficient for emulation that best of all desserts — apple pie. For only the born cook can make an apple pie. And even the born cook must know her apples before she can translate them into that luscious triumph.

That is one great advantage of owning an orchard. You start at birth, practically, to understand apples, and can proceed in what you might call apple-pie order, straight through the season from Early Harvests on until you reach that sublime pie timber, the Northern Spy.

With such an honorable succession as this at hand, the woman with flour in a barrel, lard in a crock (or butter, if you belong to the butter-*only*-for-shortening school), sugar and spice in the butt'ry, does, of course, have an advantage over the apartment dweller who buys four pounds of apples for a quarter, depending upon the grocery clerk's judgment as to their quality, and is beaten before she starts. The only way to ensure perfect success is to own an orchard. The matter of flour and shortening can be taken care of more easily, although we do recommend a hog or two, to make certain not only of proper shortening, but also of a sparerib to precede the pie.

However, and although we do, for the moment, despair
of the joy of tasting that rarest of all perfections, a green-
apple pie at its best, we might expect even from the
average cook some measure of palatable pleasure in the
lesser combinations of the same ingredients. Take, for
instance, an Apple Dowdy. The Apple Dowdy, now, is
a homely dish, and while the rule for apple pie is more
or less static, although governed by individual artistry
and a difference of opinion regarding shortening, that
for a dowdy is variable. But because of such allow-
able indulgence let no one think that any old apple-and-
dough mixture can be thrown together and bring forth
an Apple Dowdy. The intrepid Mrs. Rorer, now, as-
sembles a mixture of apples and bread crumbs and calls
that a dowdy. To my mind this is infringing upon the
rights of an Apple Betty. The dowdy that I favor is
composed of a bed of thinly sliced apples, spiced and
sweetened, enriched with butter and counterpaned with
an enscrolled circlet of dough that will flake at a touch
when baked. The principle would seem to be that of a
pie — and the surmise would be not far wrong. The difference lies in the depth of the bed, and in an almost
infinitesimal greater thickness of crust. Also you might
season with nutmeg or allspice, instead of cinnamon, if
you want to go this far.

Lest, however, you should think an Apple Dowdy *all*
straight sailing and the above rule infallible, let me tell
you of another, not a Michigan rule, but one strictly New

England. The trouble with New England dishes is that you have to have certain definite kinds of pans, pots, and utensils for different purposes. Out in Michigan we used a milk pan for scalloped oysters and potatoes, and for baked beans. We used a bread tin for cakes and meat loaves as well as for bread. Of course my father had to have his friedcakes fried in a certain iron "kittle," but then, he was n't a *cook,* he was just fussy about the cooking. A New England cook, however, must have, for instance, a pottery pan — wide, shallow, and flaring — for a clam pie, and an earthen jar for beans, as well as a special dowdy crock! To be sure, it 's called a *Pan* Dowdy, but instead of being cooked in a pan it is baked in a crock, a crock slightly smaller around the top than the bottom, and holding about a gallon. (To save me I could not get hold of a real Pan Dowdy crock in order to try this recipe properly.) And the apples must be Baldwins. Nothing short of a Baldwin will make a real, genuine New England Pan Dowdy.

Having equipped yourself with the right crock and Baldwin apples, you proceed thus: Pare your apples, quarter and core them, and heap them in your crock as high as possible. Pour over them a cup of New Orleans molasses to sweeten, and add a little water. Then take bread dough made with "empt'in's," roll it out a little thicker than for pie crust, and lay it over the top. Put the dowdy in the oven in the morning and bake until the crust is done and brown.

Take off the crust and set it aside. Leave the apples in the oven to cook slowly the rest of the day — or until late afternoon. They should cook down until the crock is about half full, a rich, red mass of sweet. Now break your crust into small pieces and stir it into the apple mixture, then set aside for the night to cool. "The crust," we are told, "soaked in the apple, becomes spongy and delicious. It is eaten with cream." If the crust, when ready to remove, was a little soft on the underside from resting on the apples, it was turned upside down on the crock, to dry and brown, before it was set aside.

If the Apple Dowdy went pretty well, you might try your hand at an Apple Frump. We are now, as you can plainly see, dealing with the bourgeois among apple desserts. An Apple Frump is in reality but a whit less attractive in appearance than an Apple Dowdy. In fact, appearance has little to do with it (as has the name), but a frump might be recommended for wash days while the dowdy could be moved up to cleaning days, or even to the spring sewing.

To make a frump you put a layer of buttered and browned bread crumbs in the bottom of a baking dish — the same, indeed, that you used for the dowdy. On these you place hot stewed apple — sliced apple, that is, stewed until tender, sweetened with brown sugar, and spiced with nutmeg or cinnamon, with the juice of a lemon added. Over the apple sprinkle a layer of seeded raisins, and on top of all put slices of bread, trimmed and generously buttered on both sides. Set this in the oven until the bread is well toasted. Serve with or without cream.

And now, just to make both frump and dowdy feel at home, let us have an Apple Fool. For this you simply bake some tart apples — according to the number you want to serve — and, while they are hot, remove pulp from skin with a fork. Mix one-half tablespoonful of confectioners' sugar, the raw yolk of one egg, and one small individual sponge cake or lady finger to each cup of the pulp, and beat all these together. Finally rub this through a coarse sieve and put in a baking dish in which it can be served. Whip the whites of two eggs to a meringue, spread evenly over the fool, and place it in the oven to brown. Serve warm or cool, — not hot, — with cream.

Having thus disposed of the more plebeian members of the Apple-Dessert tribe (of which there are something less than nine hundred and ninety-nine, which shows you what an orchard could do for you), we will step up a limb or two into the Dumpling Class.

As between a dowdy and a dumpling, — baked or steamed, — there is what might not perhaps be called a *far* cry, but something of a cry nevertheless, or at least a yelp. An Apple Dumpling is a mysterious affair.

"Very astonishing indeed — strange thing!"
(Turning the Dumpling 'round, rejoined the King.)

" 'T is most extraordinary, then, all this is.
It beats Penetti's conjuring all to pieces;
Strange I should never of a Dumpling dream!
But, Goody, tell me, where 's the seam?"
"Sire, there 's no seam," quoth she: "I never knew
That folks did Apple Dumplings sew."
"No?" cried the sterling Monarch with a grin,
"How, then, how then the devil got the Apple *in?* "

An Apple Dumpling, after an Apple Pie, was my
father's favorite apple dish and he preferred his boiled,
and of course it had to be boiled in a flannel cloth, each
pudding separate.

An old English cookbook, whose contents afford me
much pleasure, in giving a recipe for boiled dumplings
suggests that knitting the squares in which such dumplings are to be made will provide pleasant — and useful
— occupation for a lady's leisure, and will give the puddings a "very handsome appearance."

My mother, never having heard of such employment
for her leisure, had to rely upon any old piece of flannel
at hand. She did, however, wash and preserve her pudding bags after the manner of any thrifty housewife.
Once, in acceding to my father's sudden request for
boiled dumplings, she faced disaster: the pudding squares
could not be found. Nor could a single piece of any
kind of white wool whatever. The apples were peeled
and cored, and anyone versed in apple lore knows that
an apple once peeled must be used immediately to preserve both color and flavor. And not a piece of flannel

to be found. Even the last of the only old flannel sheet
in the house was gone.

My father, never far distant from the scene of action
when one of his favorite dishes was in preparation, stood
watching my mother's frantic search in a fever of anxiety.

"Ain't you got *nothin'* you can sew a dumpling into?"
he inquired impatiently.

"I can't find a thing!" Desperation tinged my
mother's voice. "And I can't see *where* the pudding
cloths — "

A spasm as of shocked recollection crossed my father's
face. His mouth fell open. He leaned upon the table.

"Have *you* done anything with 'em?" Quick to dis-
cern his passing moods, my mother flung a suspicious
eye his way.

"If they *was* pudding bags," the guilty voice admitted,
"why, I — one day I wanted to clean my gun — "

" 'Lije Thompson, you 're enough to kill a saint!" My
mother glared at him wrathfully. "Now there 's nothin'
to do but bake 'em. And serve you right."

"Wait a minute!" Fired with sudden inspiration, he
fled the room. Mother proceeded to roll and cut her
dough. An apple — cored and its centre filled with
mingled cinnamon and sugar and topped with butter —
was placed in each square of dough, the corners brought
together, the seams flattened, patted into shape.

The door burst open and my father returned, his
white fringe of hair flying, his eyes alight.

"Here!" He held aloft a garment — spread it out. "Here 's a pair of my old drawers," he cried triumphantly. "The seat 's all wore out anyway. Can't you use these? They 're flannel, and they 're clean!"

My mother snatched the garment from his hand and flung it onto a chair. "I 'm goin' to *patch* those," she said tartly, "and you 're goin' to wear 'em till spring. You 'll eat your dumplings baked!"

And he did, with nice hot lemon sauce — not too great a strain on even an impetuous man's disposition, although the boiled dumpling calls for a brandy sauce which may account for some prejudice in its favor.

In one of the old cookbooks (1845) which I have previously mentioned, I find this recipe for Sweet Apple Pudding which seems quite worthy of the eulogy accompanying it : —

"Take one pint of scalding milk, half a pint of Indian meal, a teaspoonful of salt, and six sweet apples (peeled and cored) cut into small pieces, and bake not less than three hours. The apples will afford an excellent rich jelly. This is truly one of the most luxurious yet simple Yankee puddings made."

By no means is the subject exhausted. Pies, puddings, dowdys, dumplings, frumps, fools, tarts, nests — in almost limitless succession the luscious list runs on.

Aside from its unexcelled qualities as a contributing factor to the diet in the form of such dishes as have been

mentioned, — and many others that have not been mentioned, — the apple in liquid state offered to our simple
entertainment both nourishment and pleasure. Gathering the windfalls, seconds, and otherwise least desirable
fruits from the orchard and taking them to mill was in
itself one of the most delightful occupations of autumn
days.

My father almost always went to mill on Saturdays
so that I could go along, or else, if necessity compelled him
to do otherwise, I simply did not go to school. In my
bringing up there was a wise and nice balance with regard
to what was most desirable in the way of education.
Part of mine consisted of companionship with my father.
And to that I owe much of my understanding of natural
beauty, of the laws of nature, of tolerance toward petty
and trifling ills.

And when I give myself time in which to remember
those golden days of autumn when we first filled the
wagon with bushel after bushel of apples from the fragrant orchard, and then, mounting the high spring seat,
rolled leisurely away along the narrow country road toward the mill, I am filled with regret that these poor
modern youngsters are so impoverished for opportunity
that they must draw up to a hideous little wayside stand
beside a crowded, hard-shouldered, dangerous thoroughfare to pour down their parched throats some villainous,
synthetic liquid tainted in color and insipid in taste.
How little do they know of the serene delight in jogging

along a narrow country road where upon the hazel brush
little brown fuzzy clusters are ripening, soon to be gathered along with walnuts, butternuts, and hickory nuts
and stored in the garret for winter use; of the thrill with
which we came within sound and sight — and smell —
of the old cider mill on the creek with willows and maybe
a wild crab-apple tree growing beside it. How little
can they ever know of that rich delectable flavor which
meets the eager tongue as the miller hands you a mug
of pure, unadulterated juice fresh from the mill, made
from apples grown on your own land, gathered by your
own hands.

Besides the cider in its natural and sparkling state
there was the boiled cider stored away for the enrich-
ment of mincemeat, and the cider vinegar used months
later in the preservation of countless pickles and relishes.
Cider was used also in making apple butter, gallons of
which were stored in every cellar for the embellishment
of fresh homemade bread already well coated with
fresh-churned butter.

My father did not care for apple butter. "If I 'm goin'
to have applesass," he said witheringly, "I want *sass*.
Stew up some green chips in m'lasses and it 'd taste about
the same 's that stuff." But while I would not lift a
finger to see — or taste — any apple butter that my
mother or anyone else ever made, I do know that it was
not only a valuable addition to the winter's store of

preserves, but that many people were fond of it. Hour after hour the huge kettle swinging on its iron crane in many a farmyard steamed and bubbled and stewed, its sweet and spicy aroma scenting all the air, while some-one stood guard over it, swaying the long-handled stirrer back and forth to keep the rich thickening mass from sticking to the sides.

In earlier times than ours they made a "bee" of apple-butter time, as they did of many other annual events that would otherwise have been tasks, thereby turning labor into an excuse for frolic.

But when all is said and done, the best way to eat an apple is to eat it raw, sitting if you can on the ground underneath the tree on which it grew; or, if you are still able, in a crotch of limbs suited to your form. A late October day is recommended, with blue sky, warm sun, air a pure distillation of fruity harvest. Or a day later in winter, with fruit from the apple hole outside the door, where snow and straw and good sweet earth have preserved the flavor in its finest form.

Next to the apple in its natural state comes apple pie. Apple pie and a piece of nice mild cheese. But while you may find the apple and the cheese, where will you find the pie? Such pie as my mother — and probably your mother — made.

I cannot even tell you how my mother made her pie,

for she had neither measuring spoon nor cup. If you had tried to pin her down to directions she would have told you that she never measured anything. And yet the fact is that she made more accurate measurements by far than most modern cooks will do with all the parapher- nalia at hand. Her measurements were of touch and sight guided by long experience (a most unsafe rule for the beginner in cookery) and by high standards of excel- lence. All I know about her method is that she took flour from a barrel, lard from a crock, a little salt from a jar, and blended them together into a rich crumbly mass. Then she poured water into it from a cup until she had enough. But only the born cook would know when there was enough.

In this later day there seems to be considerable argu- ment as to ingredients: whether to use bread flour or pastry flour; all lard, part lard, part butter, all butter, or a vegetable substitute for both.

In my mother's day there was less reason for con- tention. The flour came from grain raised on our own or a neighbor's field. Lard was the accepted shortening, because the day of substitutes had not yet arrived. Lard, that is, in general, although there were, among our many expert cooks, those whose creed demanded half butter, but none, so far as I know or can learn, who ran to all butter, although butter was quite as plentiful as lard. This matter of shortening is one of those "moot questions," to be settled only by experience, followed by preference — and prejudice. The whole business of making a pie crust anyway is one of artistry and skill, and honor goes to the fingers of the deft.

After the merest tossing together of ingredients on a floured board my mother broke off a portion of her dough and rolled it out, to exactly the right thickness, swept it deftly up with her rolling pin to fit the tin, patted it down with her fingers, and cut off the over-hanging edges with a knife. She peeled her apples as she used them — peeled, quartered, and sliced them into the waiting crust so they would not darken; filled the tin to a rounded nicety, pocked it over with butter, added sugar according to degree of tartness, and, if the apples themselves were lacking in flavor, sprinkled cinnamon with a miserly touch. Then she rolled out the other piece of dough and with a swirl and a dash cut an S-shaped scroll in the centre, flipped it over the pie, pinched down the edges with a capable thumb, and consigned it to the oven. Its exit from that fevered cavern was heralded by the fragrance which preceded it, growing in grace as amalgamated fruit, spice, and sugar were blended into one harmonious and odorous whole.

The pie was made early in the morning and eaten for dinner at noon, not hot, but by no means cold, fresh and reeking with honeyed sweet.

It followed upon a meal sufficiently lacking in soli-darity to warrant generous appreciation of its parts, and it was accompanied by cheese, a mild, pliable cheese of velvety texture, primrose in color, faintly reminiscent of rennet and stony-cool dairies, and served to the table in a goodly wedge with a knife to cut it.

My mother always cut the pie in half. One half was then divided into thirds, one of which fell to my share, and one my mother took. The other half was cut in two, and one piece was deposited on my father's plate; nearly a fourth of the wedge of cheese followed it. As the knife slid its pliant way through the tender crust, little creamy flakes thin as a moth's wing broke from the parent crust, too well related to the whole to drop away, too delicate in texture for blind adherence, while in its wake the golden syrup made a liquid thread of amber.

My father savored his pie leisurely, sniffing it at first lest he miss any delectable portion of its honeyed mead, however small. He ate with his knife and fitted it to his lips with a nicety unbelievable to modern dictatorial etiquette. The first quarter he ate without comment, giving himself wholly to the sensuous delight of zestful appetite. To the second he helped himself with leisurely contemplation of its grace, being now, as you might say, in a more discerning mood.

"These Greenings," he once observed critically, "make a pretty good pie, 'Miry, but they don't come up to a Spy. I 'll get you some Spies to-morrow."

"I had n't meant to make a pie to-morrow," my mother

observed, tentatively. "I'm going to wash quilts and I thought we could get along."

My father's eyes reflected shocked amaze.

"No *pie?*" Aggrieved dissentience thinned his voice. "You've made pies before now on wash day, ain't you?"

"Yes," agreed my mother, contentiously, "I have. But I'm going to do extra washing to-morrow. You can eat spice cake."

Silently my father returned to consideration of the present. A third of the second half still remained.

"Ain't either of you goin' to finish it up?" he inquired solicitously. We shook our heads. "Might's well eat it," my mother told him — as he had expected she would. "Apple pie ain't fit to use after it's stood."

And so the pie was finished. The last rich drops of syrup were spooned from the tin, the last downy flake of crust knifed from the pan. And the wedge of cheese was gone. Coffee cups and milk mug were drained.

My father drew back from the table with a gesture of fulfillment seldom allotted to mortal man.

"Pretty good pie," he admitted with a last judicial lick of the lips, "but I'll get you some Spies for to-morrow."

The orchard, as I knew it in my childhood, seems no longer to be an essential or necessary component of the farm. The invasion of worms and insects and the cost of protection have ruined the old orchards, and only those who aim to concentrate upon the apple as a commercial venture can afford its luxury. Like the pump, the pung, the old top buggy, and the organ, the orchard has sunk into that limbo of the past where only memory dwells. And as we drive through what seems to us a less opulent country than that of our childhood, we are minded of Hawthorne's lament: "And what is more melancholy than the old apple trees that linger about the spot where once stood a homestead, but where there is now only a ruined chimney rising out of a grassy and weed-grown cellar! These offer their fruit to every wayfarer, apples that are bitter sweet with the moral of time's vicissitudes."

VIII

The Full Pork Barrel

FOLLOWING apple picking, bean threshing (with flails), corn husking, Indian summer, and the fall ploughing, came butchering time. In spite of implied cruelty, this was not an altogether unpleasant season, except for the occasional sounds of distress sometimes heard when protective fingers loosed their guard upon apprehensive ears at an inopportune moment.

One never had to undergo the pangs of grief over the demise of a member of the porcine family that one felt when a pet calf or yearling "bossy" was led bleating away. Even though a tiny pig with his pink skin, curly tail, and pudgy snout is cunning in his infancy, he does not grow in loveliness, nor do his traits of character endear him as he waxes great and fat. And however much we may regret the necessity of his passing to assuage human needs, we must admit a certain satisfying exuberance attendant upon his exit.

The rites and ceremonies of "hog-killin'" naturally occurred after snappy weather had set in so that the pork could be kept fresh longer, which gave to the heating of huge cauldrons of water a certain element of coziness as well as the eternal thrill of fire building. Then there was the ominous sharpening of knives, the setting up of heavy planks on wooden horses upon which the scalded hog was laid for the divestment of his hairy covering.

There was the hunting out of old iron, heavy tin, or brass candlesticks, than which no more useful instrument has ever been devised for the "scrapin' " off of hair. And the final testing of the hog-tree or gibbet from which the carcass would hang for the last ignoble act. This was commonly called the "gamberl," a term colloquialized from the act of thrusting a pointed stick through the hog's gambrel, a tough and cartilaginous membrane at the back of the hock, for the purpose of handling and hanging.

All these preliminaries, even to the laying of the fire, were usually performed beforehand so that an early start could be made on the morning of the eventful day. Many of these were such as could profitably employ the services of children, even of a small girl — turning the grindstone, fetching kindling and cobs for the fire, and placing the candlesticks in readiness. (The advantage of the candlestick over any other instrument for scraping lay in the ease with which the shaft could be grasped, while the curved edge of the saucer made a perfect rasp.)

Housework was hustled out of the way and indoor preparations made beforehand as far as possible, for the housewife's share in the activities was but secondary

to the outside drama. Bread, pies, doughnuts, were
made and pans of beans baked, so the stove would be
left free for uses pertaining to the chief performance.

Up to the very dawn of the morning on which action
was to take place, children and dogs were greatly in
evidence, eager to lend a hand and especially to feast
curious eyes upon the gruesome preparations. But when
the morning came, when breakfast was eaten and the
menfolks in old overalls and "wam'uses" departed to
their gory task, little girls, at least, retired to some far
corner of the house where shrill screams of fear and pain
could not be heard. Sometimes, with held breath and
gooseflesh rising along arms and legs, a small child
would creep fearfully out from cover to listen appre-
hensively for the final silence which would signify an end
to the prologue, and the moment when one might safely
appear upon the scene.

No attention was paid to small boys. They must not
get in the way, but if they chose to sidle around the out-
skirts of the homely abattoir and fill their goggling eyes
with gory sight, their noses with smell of steam and sweat
and blood, and their outhanging ears with sound attendant upon the business of victualing the human family,
they could. The education of farm children begins
early.

Once the kill was over, little girls fluttered into the
arena, boys unleashed the dogs, fuel was added to the
fire, knives were tested along leathern thumbs, and tubs

and pans made ready to receive the entrails. A scene of stirring action ensued.

Each neighborhood or community had, at least within traveling distance, some one man more skilled than others in butchering, and he, in season, went from farm to farm practising his bloody craft, like any Lord High Executioner, and taking his pay as he could get it — in meat or money.

Stib Obart was the one to whose annual visit small boys and girls in our locality looked forward with ghoulish eagerness, and whose mild, rather vacuous face and long, slender, pliable hands were industriously studied for some fearful evidence of his awesome art. But quite in vain. Stib Obart was, by nature, a travesty upon his calling. He was slow-spoken, gentle, and even polite in manner, with a high-pitched, rather musical voice. Not at all the ogreish figure with bloodstained arms and hands our childish imaginations would have liked to find him.

What his full name was, or how he came to take up a profession so entirely contrary to his apparent nature, no one knew or cared. There were no analysts among us. People called him "queer," and let it go at that. My father used him, but did not like him. "Loony old coot! Too tarnation lazy to do anything else," he diagnosed Stib's disposition.

His morning's work done, Stib would pull off his overalls and shirt, scrub his hands, arms, and face with frenzied zeal, put on a clean shirt brought for the occasion, comb and brush his hair, parting it with nicety and precision in the middle, and sit down to dinner with an air of meekness and apology in no wise compatible with his occupation. And further to complicate any reasonable understanding of the man, he played the fiddle! Those same slender, delicate, knowing fingers that could thrust a dirk with deadly precision into the vulnerable point of a hog's throat could draw melody from the strings of a violin that would set the work-heavy feet of husky men to tap-tap-tapping on the floor, and bring strange lustre to the eyes of tired women who forgot their weariness in remembered youth. Or so we later learned. At the time of this particular story we had heard him fiddle, but we had not yet seen him in action. That came a little later.

"Tarnation old softy," my father dubbed him, contempt somewhat mollified by respect for skill in a calling where even the lusty spirit of men like himself quailed.

Besides Stib Obart there were generally two or three other men taking part in the "hog-killin'." My father, being a small farmer, did not keep a hired man the year round, but either exchanged work with neighboring men in busy season or employed a "hand" when needed. So when "butcherin'" time came he sent for Ol' Man Covell on the next farm, and they, with Mr. Lem Bouldry, another neighbor, did the job.

Everything was in readiness. Fire was blazing under

the huge cauldron, planks set up, knives sharpened, "gamberls" in place. Stib Obart's sleeves were rolled up, he was even running his sensitized thumb along the edge of his knife, when my father suddenly set up a hullabaloo because one of his old candlesticks was missing. Where in tunket was the other candlestick? He had one in his hand, rusty and bent half double on one side of the saucer, but the other was gone. Lem Bouldry had brought one with him; Obart had his; Covell, of course, had none. He was just that lacking in foresight and preparedness. So my father thrust the one he had into Covell's hand, and made for the house, bellowing " 'Miry!" at the top of his lungs. My mother, apprehending catastrophe, appeared at the door.

"You know where that other candlestick is?"

"How sh'd *I* know where it is!" Severely prim in her stiffly starched apron and clean calico dress, she bent questioning eyes upon him. "Ain't it where you put it last time you butchered?"

"I s'posed it was, but it ain't." He walked back to the group of waiting men, frowning, distraught. There were four hogs to be killed, four men to dress them, and only three candlesticks.

"I c'n use a knife," offered Mr. Bouldry, "and Covell c'n take my 'stick."

"Wa-al, now," drawled Covell, shoving back his old hat to scratch his head, "come to think of 't, I dunno but what I borried that candlestick one day 'bout a month ago when I 's goin' to butcher a hawg or two."

"*What!*" My father whirled upon him in such swift anger that the man actually fell back. "You mean to stand there and tell me you went into my barn and *took my candlestick* 'thout a word to me?"

The lord of a castle facing a bandit who had scaled his walls could not have been more bitterly condemnatory. Covell retired still further, but maintained some show of affront.

" 'T wa'n't nothin' but an old candlestick," he defended himself, "and you was n't to home."

For a moment my father was speechless with indignant wrath. Then, "You got it?" he demanded. "To your house — now?"

"Why — yes — I s'pose so. If I ain't brought it back — "

"Well, by cracky, you jog right home and *git* it. And when you 've got it, and brought it back, you can go home again, and *stay* there."

The man, with a grieved expression upon his face at such unreasonable asperity, slouched off toward home.

"May 's well get on," said my father gruffly. "Tarnation old fool!"

By the time the hogs were butchered and scalded the "tarnation old fool" was back with the candlestick in his hand — a disreputable thing with bristles stuck in the shank, black and dirty, but snatched into my father's eager hand as a sacred relic to a devotee.

"Could n't find another like it in twenty year," he commented feelingly while the others looked on in sympathetic understanding — all but Ol' Covell, who slouched off out of the yard with lingering looks, hoping for a leniency which was slow in coming. My father would no more have gone to Covell's barn and taken so much as a nail without permission than he would have walked into a grocery store and robbed the till, and he demanded of others the same strict observance of personal rights.

He did relent, however, and called to the man so obviously loitering. "Here," he said curtly, "you may 's well come along and git busy. But see 't you keep out o' my barn after this, 'less I 'm here."

Covell came back, a bit sheepishly, took the "scraper" which my father held out, and fell to work.

Children of to-day are skilled, vicariously, in throwing the lariat, in the frenzied excitement of the round-up and rodeo. They play "Cops and Robbers" and "G Men." They are familiar with the just or unjust deserts of the gangster and his moll. But few of them ever stood first on one small titillating foot and then on the other while a huge, inert mass of potential pork was sloshed about by use of a hog hook thrust through the victim's snout, in a vast black cauldron of boiling water, and then hauled, steaming, into the frosty air, to the improvised table of planks. There were certain compensations for being born before the days when organized crime had its part in infant education.

Divested of his bristles, a gambrel stick thrust through the tendons of his hind legs, the hog was then hoisted to the pole or tree where the final and most thrilling act of the spectacle was performed.

With murderous dirk in hand, Stib Obart gave one quick, sharp, dexterous slit to the underside of the pendent carcass; a practised hand tore the adhering membrane from the creature's sides, and the entrails were vomited forth to fall in long, undulating convolutions of gray matter into the waiting pan or tub below.

The huge, quivering mass was then carried into the kitchen and placed on a table. Over this the housewife bent, to "strip the innards," as they said in the Middle West, or, according to New England, to "riddle the guts."

The fat from these was "tried out" in one kettle while that from the "leaf" was rendered in another. This matter of rendering fat usually lasted over several days and, with its consequent spattering and odor, was one of the least agreeable details of the whole proceeding. Finally, however, when crock after crock was filled with the snowy content, firm and hard, a potential promise of crisp pie crust and smoking friedcakes, as well as exchange matter for groceries, there was that sense of satisfaction in things done that comes to all who by their own hands provide for the physical welfare of their families. And no small pleasure was to be had from the

pan of hot chitterlings or small scraps of crisp fat left
after the rendering was complete.

This, in Pennsylvania Dutch regions, mixed with
cornmeal and fried, led to the famous Philadelphia dish
called "scrapple." In our community it was sometimes
mixed with flour and baked as biscuit, or eaten in its
own crisp, amber rights.

In the final disposition of the various component parts
of the animal, livers were divided among the neighbors,
lights and hearts hung to a tree for cats and birds to
share; the tongue was set aside for pickling, and the
bladder and tail were claimed by small boys. From the
first, after it was blown up, dried, and filled with beans,
a kind of rattle was made, and from the latter a whistle.

There wasn't so much said in those days — fifty or
sixty years ago — about the "full pork barrel" as there
has been since, because it was an accepted thing. All
farmers had a full pork barrel, and most people in towns
had its equivalent, and the phrase was no metaphorical
expression of plenty. It was what you might call the
backbone of our food supply. And speaking of back-
bones in connection with the briny cornucopia of plenty
brings to my mind a pleasant contemplation of one of
the major items in the business of filling it.

The housewife of to-day has much to be grateful for
in the possession of her time-and-temperature-controlled
oven, as compared with the old black "elevated" that

stood in my mother's kitchen, a greedy and erratic con-
sumer of wood. But whether such conveniences entirely
compensate for the *spirit* with which the old bandy-
legged stove ruled the culinary end of homemaking is a
debatable question. I wonder whether the ease with
which the modern appliance turns out a properly done
leg of lamb while the mistress attends a lecture on the
"Necessity for Overhauling the Constitution of the
United States" is acceptable equation for the old-fashioned sparerib that came out of *our* oven. It is perhaps
a matter for emotion rather than a sense of efficiency and
economy to decide. Or it may be argued that the modern
mogul would crisp the porcine rib to exactly as odorous
and juicy a state of perfection as ever did that old black
wench — if it could get the rib! At any rate, there are
those of us who know what a baked sparerib was once
like, and who are often given to wondering whether
something more valuable than epicurean delight was not
lost when the utterly unreliable old kitchen wood stove
gave way to the infallibility of the electric range; when
the pork barrel resigned its place of dignity and responsibility in the cellar to a pound box of cellophane-wrapped
sausages in the ice box.

What housewife of to-day knows the delightful satisfaction of committing to the chaste bosom of her patrician
range a vast dripping pan filled to its generous depth with
fresh, full-length spareribs? No four-inch, parsimoniously pared, palely corned bone, barren of taste or flavor,

mind you, but long, slender, well-padded ribs still firmly attached to the parent spine with tenderloin intact, and the whole imbedded with savory stuffing.

And such stuffing! Modern exponents of the art of cooking, ever seeking to divert the mind of man — and particularly of woman — by new and often outlandish methods, have devised and conceived many strange combinations of ingredients under the name of stuffing. Chestnuts, which belong on the hearth or in a boy's pocket; oysters, never quite at ease except on the half-shell, in a stew or casserole; raisins, whose proper *métier* is the pudding, the fruit cake, or on the stem; cheese, the dominating flavor of which should *rule* the dish (and will) — these and other alien comestibles have been dragged in to give the hotly pursued "unusual" tang to a dish as strongly naturalized as the American eagle, only to produce a flaccid, anæmic effect where thews and sinews are indicated. For stuffing as known to old-fashioned folk in Southern Michigan, and to other epicures, is made of bread properly moistened (but not wet) with stock or milk, and characterized by mingled flavor of onion, sage, salt, and pepper, the whole generously enriched with butter.

The advent of spareribs in the days of my childhood was one of the anticipated seasonal events, like dandelion greens in spring and sweet corn in summer. They came with the first severe freeze of early winter when butcher-

ing time brought as welcome a change to the meat diet as
did a mess of greens after a winter of potato and cabbage,
and bespoke not only a delectable treat in themselves
but a round of family dinners and neighborly exchange.
For the farmers of a community usually made of butchering a succession of events in order to help each other
with the work and to keep the feast of fresh meat going
as long as possible.

The spareribs were only one of the many and varied
contributions made by the sty to the larder, but, of those
that required no treatment other than cooking, certainly
the best.

Hams and shoulders were either put in brine prepara-
tory to smoking, or given the dry-curing process, then
hung in the smokehouse to ripen under the fragrant influence of hickory sticks and corncobs. Feet and hocks
were made into "souse," and packed in small crocks to
which the liquid in which they were cooked, supple-
mented with spiced and seasoned vinegar, was added.
Owing to the gelatinous nature of this portion of the
carcass, the meat by such means was set in a quite firm
and excellently flavored jelly. "Souse," said our hired
man, "is the only good reason for a four-footed hawg."
He held, too, that souse was one of the dishes over which
a man was entirely justified in smacking his lips.

The first sight of this, while not entirely æsthetic in
nature, is certainly anything but unappetizing, especially
as served on the supper table of a simple country home,

backed by a red and white cloth, and flanked on one side by hot potatoes steaming in their jackets and on the other by a dish of freshly made kraut. To a hungry man in from clearing snow from a quarter mile or so of paths, from an hour's feeding and bedding of stock, the sight of so plebeian an array of food was anything but an offense.

The process of eating pigs' feet is not one to be encouraged in urbane society. To spear with a fork, and then attempt to hold down, a glabrous, gelatinous hock while severing the pickled meat from a bone is neither a dignified nor a satisfactory performance. A grown man, hirsute, robust, weather-flushed, would feel exceedingly futile and foolish so to wrestle with a thing that obviously calls for the able employment of the more adroit and facile human hand. Once, however, severed hock or cloven hoof is securely pinioned between thumb and finger of either hand and brought to terms with tongue and teeth, all tendencies toward proper public demeanor are forgotten in pure satiety. If some ambitious painter of the modern school of realism would attain everlasting fame at one swift, comprehensive sweep of the brush, let him give us, bent head, half-shuttered eye, arms akimbo, the portrait of "A Man Eating Souse."

From the head (including ears and snout), headcheese was made. Now whether even the most zealous back-to-the-farm-if-it-kills-us enthusiast will ever go so far as to make headcheese again is doubtful. But headcheese as made by my mother and her contemporaries was a harmonious and appetizing unification of savory meat and piquant spice. And yet nowhere in the two hundred or more cookbooks of more or less recent date that burden my shelves do I find any reference to it. But in a yellowed, thumb-marked, egg-and-molasses-stained old copy book where some faithful recorder had set forth her rules, I find the following rather dramatic account: —

"The head is singed and soaked in salt water for twenty-four hours. It is then taken out, scrubbed, and cleaned. A red-hot poker is thrust into the ears and nostrils. If large it is split in two and then placed in a kettle large enough to hold water to cover it." (At this point one's imaginative tendencies incline toward a high-held platter borne aloft by a fat-calved butler or a sandaled Salome.)

"Into the kettle are put a few bay leaves, a bunch of sage, another sprig of thyme and some summer savory, two or three onions, and a good-sized carrot cut in pieces. In a bag are put some whole spices, some peppercorns, a few cloves, and this is added to the others.

"The meat is then boiled until it drops from the bones. A thin clean white cloth is placed in a large colander and the meat is drained onto it. When quite drained it is either chopped or picked into fine pieces and packed in a bread tin. Add a very small portion of vinegar to the liquid in which the head was boiled, and pour enough of this over the meat to mould it. Over this meat place a clean dry white cloth and on top of this a weight, say a sadiron, or a stone placed on a board. Take note that the eyes, which in boiling will be removed from their sockets, are taken out and thrown to the hens."

I have never made headcheese, but there are moments when there is tranquillity to a harassed mind in the thought of fingers caressingly engaged amid a bed of herbs, including sage and savory and a sprig of thyme, preparing for a day when they will be used to flavor the detached timber from a porcine head; and other moments when the hot poker with its savage hiss and thrust offers an ameliorating hint not incompatible with one's hope of justice.

Tag ends of meat were made into sausage and the remainder of the carcass cut into convenient pieces and consigned to the pork barrel. Then after the fresh meat was gone and winter had settled down to business at zero and below, you daily visited this source of supply for the accompaniment to boiled dinners, the ubiquitous potato, a pan of beans, or, later, a mess of greens.

Of course, all such pork as was not needed for family use was hauled to the city and sold. A load of "hawgs," pink-skinned, frozen stiff, their gaping carcasses piled into the bed of the lumber wagon, was a quite usual sight in the crisp days of late fall. This would afford a little ready money, of which the farmer had so little about his house or person. His barns, his cellar, and his "butt'ry" would, without doubt, be well stocked; his family would be comparatively well, and at least warmly, clothed; there would be food in plenty.

He built a comfortable house and furnished it according to the modest standards of the day. He built barns for his hay and stock. He kept out of debt and considered a mortgage a disgrace. He did not expect to make a fortune, but he did mean to live in reasonable comfort until he died, with a respectable burial to follow. Not an ambitious programme, but one which tended toward a serene passing of his days, with a dignified exit.

There were certain seasons of the year when we could count certainly on a visit from Mr. and Mrs. Calhoun. One was in strawberry time, another was when sweet corn and melons were at their best, and again in the fall at butchering time. Of course they sometimes came in between because our farm was only nine or ten miles from Jackson, where they now lived, and although ten miles was quite a drive over sandy roads with a horse and buggy, they were so homesick for the farm life from which they had retired a few years before that they liked to come. Mr. Calhoun had once owned the second farm from us on the east, where the Bouldrys now lived, but when the boys left for the city he sold it and went to town.

They bought their potatoes and other vegetables from my father, as well as fruit, and Mr. Calhoun still thought he must put down at least half a hog. Mrs. Calhoun tried out lard and made a little sausage, just as she used to do. My father smoked the ham and shoulder for them.

"Had all a man could wish for," repined Mr. Calhoun to my father on one of his annual autumn visits, commenting bitterly on his own past fortune. "Ain't a better farm in the county than mine was, and plenty of good livin' for all of us if the boys had n't of took a notion to go to the city. Now look at 'em."

The Calhouns had two sons and two daughters. The older daughter had married an adventurous youth and gone West. They seldom heard from her. The two boys, one after the other, bitten with unrest and fired with desire for the good wages rumored by one or another of the country youth who had previously gone to work in factories, had, as they came of age, headed townward: one to Detroit, the other to Chicago. The younger girl was still at home.

At this particular time which I recall, Tom, the son in Detroit, had lost his job, and the other was living in continual fear of a crotchety boss.

"Tom don't say much," Mr. Calhoun mourned as he and my father sat talking on a pile of old lumber near the barn. "He 's too proud. And I don't know whuther he wishes he 's back on the farm or not, but we can see he 's plum scared of winter comin' on. He says he 's sure to get another job right away, but I hearn tell there 's a good many men out of work in Detroit, and in Chicago

too. And they got rent to pay — both of 'em. *Rent!*"
He spat the despised word from between compressed
lips. "Havin' to pay *rent* when here he'd a had a home
long's he lived — him and his childern too. Coal to
buy! And forty acres good wood there was to cut.
And three small childern, Tom's got, and Bill two.
Buyin' milk! Quart to a time!"

To the hopeless scorn in his voice my father made no
reply. His face, however, was long and sad. He picked
up a new chip and whittled it into strips.

"Bill," continued Mr. Calhoun bitterly, "out to Chicago, don't know what minute *his* job 'll be gone. Ma
wrote to both of 'em to come home for Thanksgivin', but
they both wrote they couldn't make it. They ain't got
the money, 's the fact, but 'course they won't admit it.
Ma wants to send 'em their fare, but I said no. Let
'em sweat. Mebbe they'll come to their senses. We'll
send 'em the fixin's, but to think of *our* boys not havin'
plenty! Makes me sick!"

And sick he looked. To a farmer whose days had
been one long succession of plentiful living, the very
thought of a meagre supply on the day of feasting was
more than he could bear.

"I's a fool ever to sell the farm," he commented un-
happily. "*I* didn't hev to give up work, if they did
want to. I wa'n't sixty then, hale and hearty as ever.
Healthier 'n I've been since — and happier. If I'd a
kep' it they'd had a home now anyway. But Ma'd

worked hard all her life and I thought if *they* 's goin' to have things so soft and easy for their wives Ma ought to have no less."

"She like it?" asked my father, not lifting his eyes.

"She never let on to me *once*," Mr. Calhoun got up, pulled his coat up onto his shoulders, and settled his hat on his white head, "till last night. I was down suller gettin' a can of cherries for a pie, and I said somethin' about her havin' as much fruit on her shelves as she ever did on the farm and asked her what she wanted to do up so much for when she did n't hev to. She said she 'd ruther put up fruit and vegetables than set around lookin' out a window and see a lot of discontented folks traipsin' by. And she — cried!"

He took a turn down the greensward for a few feet and then came back looking like a thundercloud. He was very tall and his shoulders humped over. My father just kept on whittling till the chip was all gone, then he shut up his jackknife and put it in his pocket.

"She cried," Mr. Calhoun went on, "and said she 'd never wanted to leave the farm. She done it because she thought I was gettin' too old to farm it alone."

Both men were silent. A chipmunk ran under the woodpile and Shep got up and began to claw the wood and earth after it.

"Why'n't you buy you a small place?" said my father after a while. "You could farm it a little and truck it same 's I do."

Mr. Calhoun was older than my father, but both men were rugged and you did not think of age in connection with either.

"I 've thought of it," said Mr. Calhoun earnestly, "but that would n't help the boys now. We 'd ought to have kept it."

Mrs. Calhoun came to the door and told him they 'd better go. They still kept a cow, as so many farmers did after they retired and went to town to live, and they had to go home to milk. My father got up and the men started off to get the horse.

"I 'd give my eyeteeth," said Mr. Calhoun, "to be killin' my own hawgs, haulin' in punkins for the cattle, huskin' my own corn. Stren'th! It don't take near so much stren'th to *work* — not when you 're workin' for your own folks — 's it does to set around wishin' you had work to do. *Work* don't hurt nobody."

They went to the barn, got the horse, and hitched him to the buggy. They led him up to the horse block and filled the back of the buggy with apples, a Hubbard squash, some "beggies," a punkin, and a piece of fresh pork. My father would deliver half a hog. Mrs. Calhoun was going to make sausage herself. They all shook hands — they shook hands with me — and drove away. I thought they looked sad.

My father took the milk pails off the shelf. I got my little tin mug and we started for the barn. My mother came out to the woodpile to get some wood.

"You let that be," said my father, — and I thought his voice sounded very gentle, — "and I 'll fill the wood box when I get through milkin'." He stopped and looked at her. He wanted to say something, but words come hard to country folk. The growing dusk helped him.

"*We* ain't got much, 'Miry," he said huskily, "but what we got 's our own."

My mother gathered up an apronful of chips and straightened.

"We got enough," she said briefly. "When I get my shelves full of pickles and preserves, the bins full of potatoes and apples, and the pork barrel full, I know nothin' very bad can happen to us. That 's more 'n a lot of folks can say."

With such an attitude the progressive mind of to-day would have small patience. And yet, if one could probe the inner recesses of the human heart and get the truth from it, I wonder how many of the present restless generations would not like to sit down to a dinner of which the basic quality savored of the full pork barrel in their own cellar.

IX

Shot Bag and Powderhorn

THE shotgun or musket was as customary a part of the farmer's accoutrement in his design for living as the plough or scythe. The gun was either slung from a couple of wooden pegs on the kitchen wall or stood behind the kitchen door. The log cabin, where at least one musket decorated the wall above the fireplace, with others at equally strategic points, had, before my time, in general given way to the frame house with kitchen stove, and while the trusty musket was no longer needed as protection against predatory Indian or dangerous beast, it still had its place among the implements used in providing for human needs. A powderhorn, usually salvaged from the barnyard abattoir, and a shot bag of home-tanned leather also formed part of the wall decoration. Not so much, in all probability, as means of ornamentation as to be handy.

Steel traps, out of season, hung in bunches in barnyard or woodshed, and in season the pelts of woodchuck, muskrat, beaver, coon, squirrel, fox, and occasionally a lynx, sprawled against some outer wall. The skunk, or,

as he is more politely called, the polecat, had not yet
come into his own as a fur-bearing animal, but was
highly regarded as a source of oil for congested lungs and
water-soaked boots. The meat of certain of these animals provided no small part of our cuisine.

My father was no Nimrod and, while fishing was a
favorite pastime with him, for hunting he had no special
flair, and therefore our own table was perhaps not so
plentifully supplied with diversity of meat as were those
of some of our neighbors. I have always thought that
his love for animals of all kinds was responsible for his
lukewarm attitude toward this nutritional source, although I never heard him make any critical comment
on the pursuit on the part of others. For trapping,
however, he had no use whatever except for luring the
rabbits that ate his young lettuce, into a "Figger 4" —
a harmless device which put the consequences straight
up to the trapper. Either you had then to kill the
creature in cold blood or let it go. Inasmuch as we were
never overstocked with rabbit meat I must assume that
he was a poor contriver. But for the wily woodchuck
he had no leniency. My father was a pretty good shot
even if he was no hunter, and always threatened that if
one of these crafty beasts showed himself on the second
of February where he could see him, he 'd blow his
"tarnation head plumb off. He 'd never see his tarnation
shadder a *second* time!" But I cannot remember any
evidence of one less groundhog on that particular day,

although every year there were several pelts to my father's credit hanging on the woodshed wall, especially as the early corn thrust its green spikes above the ground and a fat, arrogant little figure would be seen sitting impudently upright on its squat haunches to reconnoitre the field. Then, unless he was quicker on the exit than my father on the trigger, he got his "tarnation head blown plumb off."

Not only would my father do no trapping himself with steel, but he would allow none on his land if he knew it. Fair warning was given, but even so, Old Covell once laid traps along the riverbank, the presence of which was made known when Shep, one moonlit night, set up a piteous wailing which took my father out of bed at a bound and into pants, boots, and overcoat in less time than it takes to tell it, or so it seemed. Out of the door he went, jamming his old fur cap down over his bald head while my mother and I, shivering in our nightgowns, watched from the window.

In a few minutes he was back, walking slowly to accommodate a whimpering, limping dog, and with a steel trap dangling from his hand.

The dog, who never, except in the coldest weather, would accept the hospitality of the house, came teetering in at his heels on three legs, the fourth hanging pitifully loose, crushed and bleeding.

My father took off his old coat and laid it on the floor, then laid the dog, unprotesting, upon it. My mother brought a basin of warm water and rags, and the arnica bottle. The foot was bathed, anointed, and bound. The dog whimpered, licked his master's hand, and lay still upon the coat.

My father said little. I do not even know what he said to Old Covell when he took the trap home next day. But I do know that no more traps were set upon our land.

Because of such seeming lack of enterprise on the part of our natural "pervider" I had not much opportunity to see the art of cooking game practised in my own home. One of the times I came closest to actual demonstration was not, according to my notions, entirely satisfactory in results. The incident occurred along in the early spring of the year when I must have been about eight years old. I came home from school hungry as a child could be who had walked a mile in frosty weather with nothing but a cold lunch to bridge the gap since breakfast. I opened the kitchen door to be greeted by the most heavenly odor of roasting meat that can be imagined. Not frying pork, either fresh or salt, not even chicken, but *meat,* fresh, savory, sweet, sizzling meat.

"Oh, Mother!" I cried delightedly. "What *is* it? Can I have some? *Now?*"

" 'T is n't meat," declared my mother, coming forward as she always did to take my tin dinner pail and help with my wraps. "Leastways, it is n't meat to *eat*."

Hungry, tantalized by the exquisite and unusual

aroma, I burst into tears. My father, opening the door at that moment, wanted to know the trouble. I told him, sobbing. I wanted some of that good-smelling m-m-meat!

"Well," said my father, wrinkling his own nose appreciatively in the direction of the old elevated oven, "it *does* smell good." Then, turning to my mother, "Why don't you give her some? Ain't it done?"

"You know she can't have it," pronounced my mother irritably. "It 's skunk's meat and you know it."

"What if 't is?" inquired my father imperturbably. "Ain't no law against skunk meat 't I 've heard. Le 's have some." And he started toward the oven, only to be defeated by the mistress of the kitchen, who fended him off with a dramatically outstretched arm.

"You ain't goin' to feed that child none of that meat, 'Lije Thompson," she cried, "not if I have to throw it out of doors."

"Well," said my father tartly, "if you ain't goin' to do anything else with it you might 's well throw it out of doors. What 's the matter with it?"

"You make me so *mad* sometimes, 'Lije," — my mother was near to tears herself, — " 't I could — could — you *know* I 'm only tryin' it out to get the grease."

"Gettin' the grease out ain't goin' to hender the *meat* from bein' et, is it?"

"It was n't *cleaned* to cook. I did n't even wash it. *You can't have it!*"

"Get it out o' sight and hearin' then," ordered my father sternly if illogically, "and we'll go out and kill us a hen. C'mon, dawtie."

Our neighbors, however, especially the Bouldrys, who had several boys, frequently shared with us the spoils from gun and trap. There was apparently but a short closed season, if any, and that especially for birds in nesting time. I do not remember ever seeing the clouds of passenger pigeons that migrated to the North each spring to breed, but my father often told of the marvelous sight of millions of birds in the air, their coming heralded by a flapping of wings that sounded like thunder, and making a cloud so thick that the sun was hidden. It sometimes took an hour for them to pass over, the flock extending as far east and west as you could see.

The passenger pigeon, I am told, looked very much like the mourning dove whose tender plaint is still heard in Michigan, except that the former were larger and the male was very pretty with a red breast.

Of course when such a flight was in progress shotguns were hastily snatched from the wall and any low-flying birds were soon food for man. Roasted, stewed, or fried, they were of excellent flavor — a dark meat and somewhat tough, requiring a longer cooking than tame pigeons.

While I do not remember the flight of the passenger pigeons, I do well remember the semiannual flight of numerous flocks of wild geese and ducks. The latter often peppered the small lakes in our vicinity, especially when they were on their way South in the fall, and the popping of guns in early morning was a familiar sound.

The wild geese honk-honking their way over our heads in their symmetrical V-shaped flight were a prophecy and a sign most welcomed in the spring. "Well, saw a flock of geese to-day — won't be long now." Sometimes they would be flying so high in the early morning that we could not see them, only hear the eerie guiding cry of the leaders as they kept the ranks in file, signifying their passage. There would sometimes be as many as eighty or a hundred in a flock, and a dozen or more flocks in a day.

Farmers did not much encourage tame pigeons, but they did not need much encouragement. The children enjoyed them and they bred so rapidly that in many flocks of barnyard fowls a number of pigeons would be seen feeding. Grain was plentiful, and no more thought was given to the quart or two of extra feed thrown out for the pigeons than the extra pan of milk that was set down for the barn cats.

The Bouldry boys had built a special loft for pigeons, for Mr. Bouldry would not countenance their fouling his hay, and pigeon pie was a not infrequent delicacy on their table. In running down ways and means by which the housewives made pigeon pie, I find that Mrs. Bouldry made hers pretty much after this fashion: —

The birds were disjointed, wiped with a damp cloth, and cooked until tender in boiling salted water with an onion and a sprig of thyme. They were then drained and put in a deep baking dish, the liquid strained and poured over them. To this a cupful of cream, a tablespoonful of butter, and a tablespoonful of flour, mixed together, were added. The pie was then covered with a rich pastry crust and baked until brown.

The squab, which is the pigeon in the early stage of its adolescence, is broiled or fried — one to each person. It is first plucked, singed, drawn, and split down the back, but not *through* the back, flattened and sprinkled with salt and pepper. Butter — about two thirds of a tablespoonful to a squab — is blended with an equal amount of flour, and this mixture is rubbed over the birds, inside and out. They are then laid in a shallow baking pan and put in a hot oven for from forty minutes to an hour. They should be basted every ten minutes or so with hot water and butter — two tablespoonfuls of butter to half a cup of water. When browned they are served hot on a piece of toast which has been buttered and seasoned with salt and pepper. To-day I should garnish the plate with a sprig of watercress, but Mrs. Bouldry would never have thought of it, even though the cress grew in the brook that flowed through their yard.

Wild duck — canvasback, mallard, and redhead — have very little fat on them and should be larded with salt pork across the breast, and basted with the hot water and butter. Directions for larding can be found in any well-ordered cookbook.

All wild fowl are strongly flavored, with a suggestion of fish. To temper this flavor, soak the fowl after pluck-ing, singeing, and drawing, in quite strong salt water, for an hour. Then wash in hot soda solution, and dry with a woolen or outing-flannel cloth. Moreover, all such fowl are better when hung and ripened for several days after killing, in a cold place, before they are used — a procedure contrary to that for domestic fowl, which are the better for immediate, or reasonably immediate, use. Wild fowl, too, need strong seasoning in cooking: the tang of black pepper, onion, thyme, and savory, sprinkled inside and out.

To cook wild duck, after the first preparation (the soaking in salt water, washing again in hot soda water, the sprinkling outside and in with salt and pepper), truss the wings and neck, lard the breast with salt pork, brush with melted butter, and sprinkle lightly with flour. Stuff as for any poultry, but *using no sage* — that is, with a bread stuffing not too moist but with a little chopped onion and a sprinkling of thyme. Place the fowl in a baking pan with half a cup of water and bake in a hot oven for about twenty minutes, or until tender. Epicures prefer their wild fowl not too well done. Serve with applesauce — tart apples, peeled, cored, cut into eighths, and cooked until clear but not to the breaking point; sweeten and season, if desired, with a little all-spice.

Wild goose is cooked after the same rule as tame goose. With goose, as with wild duck, cook just until the blood does not run and until the flesh is tender, but not to the point considered desirable for domestic fowl.

Grouse and quail are roasted in the same manner. Rub with butter and broil for about ten minutes. Serve on toast.

A tart jelly should be served with all wild fowl — currant, cranberry, rhubarb, or wild plum. Spiced currants are also good.

Boys, in the days of my early country life, were adept in the art of dressing — and sometimes pretty good at cooking — the small furry animals such as squirrels and rabbits of which there were great quantities. They would run a sharp knife around the middle of the body and "peel off his britches," as they said, stripping the skin from his hind quarters, then "yank off his gloves."

These small animals were either fried or stewed. In either case the meat is cut up and soaked in cold salted water for an hour. To fry, wipe it dry on a flannel cloth, season with salt and pepper well rubbed in, roll in beaten egg, then in flour or cracker crumbs, and fry in plenty of hot fat — butter, pork fat, or oil — until tender. Only very young animals should be cooked in this way.

To stew, follow the directions for frying, but put into a heavy kettle (what you will do without an old iron kettle I do not know!) with a few slices of bacon, a sliced onion, a cup of stock or clear soup, half a glass of currant jelly, and cook slowly until tender — from one to two hours, depending upon age. Water must be added in small amounts as it boils away and the meat begins to fry. (Melt a little butter in the water used for this purpose.) Keep closely covered.

Either rabbit or squirrel pie is made in much the same way, except that after the meat is tender it is put in a baking dish with the liquid, covered about two thirds with hot water (including the liquid), and topped with pastry crust. Small holes should be cut in the top to let the steam escape.

Coon hunting was (and still is) a sport frequently indulged in by country boys, and when we were wakened on a frosty moonlit night by the yelping of the hounds, we would say, "They've treed a coon." The boys hunted for the pelts, but those who have eaten the meat say it is excellent.

No license was required for hunting deer in those days and there was no age limit. The height of a boy's ambition was to get to an age when the men would let him go with them on a deer hunt. There were no deer left in our part of the state by the time I came along, although our grandmothers told of days when they ate up

the cabbages in the garden and "tromped" down the
flower beds. When I was a little girl, however, men
and boys went "up north" — north of Jackson, that is
— a hundred miles or more. They took a train at
Jackson for some point north, from whence a lumber
train or an ox train would take them to their destina-
tion. Because of the luxury of any kind of travel, deer
hunting was not as common then as it is now. Venison
therefore was an extreme rarity with us, although some
of the boys and men in the vicinity went each year,
and often we would be so fortunate as to share in the
results.

One year my father's niece, Adelaide, sent word to us
that they had been "up north" and had brought back a
fine big deer. She asked us to come over on the following Sunday and have some of it for dinner. Tingling
with excitement, we drove on Sunday to Adelaide's.

This, as it turned out, was a most special occasion,
because this year Big Jim, instead of taking one or
two of the older boys as was his custom, had taken
Adelaide and Cory, only a little older than I, and the
youngest boy, fourteen. Big Jim had a brother living
up north — farther north than most of the hunters went
— who made his living hunting, fishing, and trapping.
They knew he lived in a wild place, but just how wild
they did not know until they went.

They took the train at Jackson as usual and rode all
day, until late in the afternoon. It was the last of

October and dark came early. When they got off the train there was Big Jim's brother with a lumber wagon and a yoke of oxen to meet them. It was well he had a wagon, for they had brought many bags of provisions, such as potatoes, apples, vegetables, a sack of sugar, some coffee, and a good many other things that they knew woods people could not easily get.

The wagon was loaded — with provisions and people. Buffalo robes were given Adelaide and the children, for it was cold — freezing — and it would be a long ride. Nine miles, Big Jim's brother said, but Adelaide said it seemed more like ninety miles. Most of the way was over a corduroy road, — logs thrown across wet and marshy places and covered with hay, — and Adelaide said she did n't believe she had a whole bone in her body when she got there. And the children were scared out of their wits. Wolves ran in front of them and howled, and once, when something made a worse crashing sound than usual, Big Jim's brother said it was a bear.

There was, fortunately, a very bright moon, — the hunter's moon, — and they could see the woods on either side looking dark and fearsome. They could often see bright fiery eyes watching them from the undergrowth, and once they heard a terrible cry that made their blood curdle and sent them shivering down underneath the robes. Big Jim's brother said it was a "painter."

Adelaide said it was the longest, coldest, most awful nine miles she ever hoped to travel, but that when they got to the log cabin in the woods where Big Jim's brother and his wife lived there was a big fire on a hearth and the smell of roasting meat and coffee. She said she never smelled anything better in her life, and she never expected anything would *feel* better, even if she should rest on "flowery beds of ease" in Heaven, than did the bed when they finally turned in. And it was nothing but a bed made of pine branches at that.

Not only had Big Jim brought home the big deer, but they had brought the head and neck of another — a huge buck with widespread antlers — which young William, the oldest son, said he was going to take to town the next day to have embalmed and mounted.

"How 'd you like *that*, Uncle 'Lijer?" he asked boastfully, taking credit to himself for his father's prowess, measuring the antlers, poking at the staring eyes.

"I would n't like it," said my father shortly, and turned away. "I 've things enough to trouble me as 't is."

William was concerned. "You don't think it 's *wrong* to shoot deer, do you, Uncle 'Lije?" he asked anxiously. "There 's lots of deer."

"No," said my father more gently, "I don't think it 's wrong at all. I think it 's *right* — to shoot what you want to eat. I 'm goin' to eat some of that venison and *lick my chops*. But I don't want the eyes of no dead critter who might of been a relation follerin' me around."

The venison we had for dinner was roasted, and from what I remember hearing, and from what I have learned since by experience, the method is approximately this: The meat is first wiped with a heavy cloth wrung from a weak solution of vinegar and water. Venison is a dry meat and should be well larded with thin strips of salt pork or brushed with melted butter and sprinkled with salt. Lay it in the roaster bottom side up and roast for half an hour at a temperature of 450 degrees. Then lower the heat to 375–400 and cook until slightly tender; allow twenty minutes to the pound and baste frequently with hot water and melted butter. When half done dredge lightly with flour and salt, then as it begins to brown spread currant jelly over the top and add a little water and butter to the pan. It must be kept moist by frequent basting.

Venison roast should be served hot with a sauce made by melting a fourth cup of butter in a saucepan until sizzling hot. Stir in a tablespoonful of flour until smooth and slightly brown. Add two tablespoonfuls of currant jelly, two of minced parsley, salt and pepper. Or use sherry wine instead of the jelly and serve either red or black currant jelly with it, or wild plum jam.

Venison steak should be cut about half an inch thick, brushed with melted butter, seasoned with salt and pepper, and broiled on a greased grid. Serve on a hot platter and pour over it the sauce given above. Use watercress to garnish, and serve currant jelly.

Adelaide, of course, had no temperature-controlled oven by which to gauge her heat, but the old wood stove managed, nevertheless, to turn out as juicy, savory, and delicious a piece of roasted meat as I ever remember — except that which was roasted in our old elevated and which, to my everlasting regret, I was not allowed to taste.

Neither had Adelaide cress with which to garnish — that is, like Mrs. Bouldry, she would no more have thought of putting cress on the platter with her meat than she would a tuft of clover. In the sight of her ribald family the one would have been as appropriate as the other. But she did have the currant jelly, both red and black, and she knew how to use it.

A generous hunk of venison carefully wrapped in clean linen was stowed in the back of our buggy when we started for home. So was a good-sized ham, salted and smoked and sewed into a canvas bag.

"Far as I 'm concerned," remarked my father ungratefully as we jogged along towards home, "if I had to choose — they could keep their venison so long as I can have the ham."

X

A New Home and an Oyster Supper

ALTHOUGH our home was nearly a thousand miles from the nearest habitat of the oyster, we were not unacquainted with that succulent bivalve. Not, however, as he is known to-day to inland as well as to coast, armored by nature or even dished up raw and cold from the refrigerated tank, but protected from contamination by a coat of tin.

I could have been hardly more than five years old when I first saw one of these square-shouldered, sharp-angled cans. Ours was a conservative family, however, considerably dominated by my father's prejudices, such as his antipathy toward tomatoes, and it may quite likely be that anything so foreign to his limited acquaintance, and so peculiarly housed, had met with the refusal of his countenance, if, indeed, it had come to his attention at all. That I do not know, but I do know that meeting these oyster cans through the neighborly overtures of Ol' Man Covell would have given them no advantage.

Once in a while, however, the man rendered what turned out to be a definite service, and the introduction of tinned oysters to our humble diet was one of them. Since his farm lay east of ours he had to pass our house coming home from town, and on one cold stormy day in winter he stopped at our house first, in itself an unprecedented thing to do.

My father was at the barn doing evening chores and my mother met Mr. Covell at the door. He was holding out a parcel wrapped in brown paper.

"Brought you suthin', Miz' Thompson," he said, smiling broadly. "Our folks had some last week and we thought they 's lickin' good."

"What is it?" My mother took the package thrust toward her and felt its rigid surface.

"It 's a can of oysters," replied Old Covell heartily. "You ever tasted 'em?"

My mother hesitated. "Why, no," she said, "I have n't. How much are they?" Her own sense of obligation, or else her certainty of my father's prickly resentment at what he would call the "old coot's officiousness," outweighed both curiosity and gratitude.

"Nothin'. Nothin' at all." Old Covell gestured largely with his huge, unmittened hands. "We liked 'em so well Ma wanted me to get some, so I got you some too."

"I don't know 's I 'd know what to do with 'em," my mother said doubtfully, still fingering the package and debating the advisability of acceptance.

"You just heat up some milk and cream," he told her competently, " 'bout a quart or so, and then you put the oysters in, likker 'n' all, and fetch it t' a boil. Then you put in some salt and pepper and a good hunk of butter, and by Crimus you never tasted anything like it. Nor smelt, either. You eat 'em with crackers. You open it where it 's thin."

My mother thanked him uncertainly and closed the door. She opened the can with skeptical fingers, but as the dull knife penetrated the end of the can and a most tantalizing odor filtered forth upon the warm air of the kitchen she sniffed, first experimentally, then eagerly. I sniffed — and I have never smelled anything since that equaled the tickling appetizing fragrance of that first tin can of oysters, unless it was that of all the other tin cans of oysters which followed. For not only did my father fail to refuse the hospitality of neighbor Covell's gift, but he fell, at the first opening of the door, an eager victim, first to the odor that seduced his nose, and then to the taste that cajoled his palate; and as long as he lived, oysters in every known form of cookery, as well as raw, were amongst the delights of his fastidious taste. And yet he never saw one that did not come out of a tin can.

It remained for a little later date, however, to show us the real ambrosial heights to which this humble tenant of a deep that we never knew could scale.

When I was somewhere between ten and twelve, we moved. My father was past seventy now — and while he was hale as ever, the old farm was more than he cared to till. Most of it had been in meadow and hay for a number of years, while he had confined himself to that form of land culture which he enjoyed most — the growing of small fruits and vegetables. So now he finally yielded to the urging of Aunts Hanner and Sophrony to sell the farm and move over nearer them into the little town of Millbrook. A few acres here of unusually fertile soil already bearing a number of fruit trees, with a house much more convenient than the old one, although never so dearly loved, gave less work and greater comfort.

It was not without sadness that we left the old farmhouse where I had been born and where we had known great content. My mother, not given to idle tears, wept a little as she went about packing up her simple belongings, and my father's face wore an expression of grim dejection while gathering his late crops, picking up and piling together tools, tag ends of harness, fishing tackle — all the accumulation of years.

However, there was also the feeling of adventure, change, and excitement, of which there had been but little in our lives. We should live in town! Or close to town, which was the same thing, and to people. (I should speak only for my mother and myself, and not for my father, who hated both change and towns.) Of course Millbrook was but a village and a small one at that, but we did not speak of "villages" in Michigan, or "hamlets." It was "town," and the size did not so much matter. We should live near the Aunts Hanner and Sophrony, and also Big Jim's family, with all its good friendly noise and confusion. And there would be the village school with strange teachers and new acquaintances — an anticipation fraught with both eagerness and apprehension.

Nevertheless, I can distinctly remember a feeling of alarm as I saw our rooms being dismantled: our beds torn apart and ruthlessly bundled into a lumber wagon; the kitchen stove hoisted ignominiously into the back end; my mother's chair carelessly tossed atop. I felt as if secure and familiar ground were being torn from underneath my feet and I clung — annoyingly, no doubt — to my mother's side or tagged at my father's heels, dumb and miserable as the day of our moving went by. Even Shep sensed the unusual activity and fawned and whimpered until my father booted him — but not unkindly — from his feet.

"Git out the way, you tarnation old fool," he scolded. "*You* won't get left behind." But Shep took no chances and crawled underneath the loaded wagon, where he stayed until the horses were hitched to it and it moved away.

Remembering that sensation of impending disaster, of the sudden loss of that security and stability I had always, although quite unconsciously, felt in my home and in its sure and familiar surroundings, and the shock it was to be thus rudely torn from the ground where all my roots were fixed, I wonder what it does to modern childhood to be tossed from pillar to post, or what that childhood lacks that never knows the meaning of stabilized living.

Mr. Bouldry was moving us with his own wagon and a span of fine big dappled grays to draw. Percherons, they were, a breed of work horses recently imported, with handsomely arched necks, heavy manes, fatly rounded rumps, and great shaggy clumps of coarse hair at their hocks.

They started early in the morning, and Miz' Bouldry came over to bring us a basket of food for breakfast and another of cold food for our lunch — fried chicken, a loaf of bread, a pan of beans, pickles, pie. Miz' Covell came over too, and all the girls, bringing a pail of "m'lasses" cookies (and without, as my mother remarked afterward, having borrowed the "m'lasses" to make them!) and a pork cake so generously enriched that even Shep turned away his nose.

Old Covell had been hanging around ("Nosin' ol' coot!" my father growled) ever since the packing up had begun, not offering to help, but generous with advice and suggestions, hands in his pockets, the everlasting cud of tobacco in his cheek.

My mother, my father, and I went in the democrat wagon in the back of which were a trunk with our clothes, clothes baskets of bedding, and a barrel of dishes. To the rear of the wagon, Rosy was tied. Rosy was our best cow, — the others had been sold, — and faithfully she plodded along behind, her cloven hoofs pumping steady little plops of dust in the sandy road, her tail occasionally switching off a roving fly. Once in a while she would slow her pace a little to bellow a lonesome protest, but the horses drove steadily ahead paying no attention to her homesick plaint.

At noon we stopped to eat. The horses were un-hitched by the side of the road, tethered to the fence, and given their oats. Rosy's rope was fastened to a tree, under which she was allowed to browse. My mother spread our lunch on a red and white checked cloth where the roadside lifted to a bank, and grate-fully we thought of our old neighbors and their friendly contribution to our comfort. Even Miz' Covell's hope-less gesture brought an appreciative word from my mother. "She *means* well," she said, "but she can't boil water." The pork cake was left uncut.

It was a beautiful day in October, and while I hold no brief for the beauties of the Middle West as against the natural charms of Eastern states, I do maintain that on a warm October day when the very air is a filmy veil, gold-colored like dandelion wine, it has a haunting loveliness hard to beat.

On such a day the rounded maples march along the roadsides in single rhythmic file, a mass of jonquil yellow, with here and there dissenting crimson flinging

ruddled leaves to deepen the spreading carpet underneath their thinning boughs.

On such a day the woodbine runs like a garnet thread
along the fences of meadows, greened by recent rains,
embroidering the fields of yellow stubble paled by tor-
rid sun, or where the corn is cut and shocked, ready
to be husked. And like a sudden, high, thrilling note
in symphony, the golden sassafras lifts its head — the
aromatic, eccentric sassafras with its three-lobed leaves
and its jeweled blue and crimson fruit, which accentu-
ates the glory of the vine, thus still more vigorously
outlining the dividing lines. Thence it roves vagrantly
to dusty roadside where the ruddy sumac glows and
burns against the russet brown of hazel brush, whose
furry little clumps of hidden nuts await the frost. Further embroidering the narrow banks, like galloons of
colored lace, is the creeping blackberry, the emerald
of its leaves changing to rose, to rust, to deep maroon.

On such a day as this we packed away the remainder
of our noonday lunch and tucked it again in the back
of our spring wagon; my father backed the horses to
the tongue, and retied Rosy to the rear. We climbed in,
my father "g'langed" and "giddapped," and we were off
to the new home.

Our new home was neither on the main road leading
to Jackson nor on the main street of the village, but on
a short crossroad that broke off the north and south road
perhaps an eighth of a mile from the town. The house

was larger and more convenient than that we had left. In it we had both a parlor and a sitting room, besides dining room and kitchen and several bedrooms — an unnecessary amount of space, but not altogether unwelcome to my mother, whose latent social instincts had of necessity been held in check. The kitchen, while not quite so large as the big one on the farm, was still sizable enough to allow for my mother's rocker and the table where my father preferred to have his meals. The huge faded "Map of the World," on which I had learned my letters, found its accustomed place on the wall, as did the steeple clock and its shelf, underneath which continued to hang the annual collection of almanacs. As a matter of fact, it turned out very well and we all became fond of our new home, which only goes to prove the amenity of the human mind to adjustment, and probably, also, the advantages of occasional change.

The régime of living was now considerably altered. No longer was there any need of making switchel to carry to the hayfield, although my mother still continued the custom of carrying a mid-morning lunch to my father wherever he was working, and, on churning days, a pitcher of his favorite beverage, buttermilk. He continued to keep a cow because he would not trust his love of good butter and stone-churned buttermilk to even the best butter hand in the country. He kept no hogs, but bought one each fall and did his own curing and salting, while my mother kept her hand in at sausage,

headcheese, and souse. They fed a sufficient number of
fowls to supply eggs, broilers, and chicken for pie and
fricassee, but the Thanksgiving turkey and the Christmas goose came from neighboring farms, not, however,
dressed as for market, but purchased long enough in advance to be confined and fattened under the eye of a
critic versed in the flavor of edible birds.

We had left the Bouldrys and Covells and Miz' Lury
Lane, who had always helped my mother in emergencies,
a few miles behind, although Miz' Lane still continued
to come for several days at a time during spring housecleaning or at the height of the fruit season, and between
ourselves and the Bouldrys Sunday visits were sometimes
exchanged. Miz' Lou Esty also came occasionally for
a visit, if not in the rôle of seamstress. As for the
Covells, my father said the only thing that consoled
him for leaving the farm which we had all so loved was
"gettin' shet of their shif'less borrowin', and the sight of
a swill pail on the front stoop." It probably was not
quite as bad as that, but the appearance of their place
was sufficiently unkempt to warrant the extravagance of
expression.

Many and exciting were the new experiences that
confronted us, but one of the chief of these was the
custom of visiting Uncle Matt and Aunt Martha once
a month to attend the oyster suppers given by the
Glass Ball Shoot to which Uncle Matt belonged — and

where colored glass balls were used instead of clay pigeons.

Uncle Matt and Aunt Martha were among the several cousins and second cousins of my father who made up the Thompson clan, which was scattered over several townships of Jackson County in Southern Michigan. Uncle Matt was a prosperous farmer, but their home, being some fourteen or fifteen miles or so from where we had lived, had been too far away for frequent visiting; now we were considerably nearer, and to my mother's obvious surprise my father fell in with the invitation from Uncle Matt and Aunt Martha to spend Saturday night with them and go to the Shooting Club with less grumbling and fewer arguments than anyone, knowing his antipathy to evening capers, could have expected. My mother said she thought the Sunday-night suppers at the Larrabee home in our old neighborhood had had a good deal to do with it. He had made enough fuss about going there, heaven knows.

At any rate when Uncle Matt and Aunt Martha, the first time they came to see us after we moved to Millbrook in the fall, asked us to come over there the day of the opening shoot, my father said yes. Uncle Matt was one of his favorites among the cousins, although he was several years younger than my father, and Aunt Martha was one of the best cooks in the county, as well as being a very pleasant and comfortable woman. It was a nice place to visit.

Uncle Matt lived west of Millbrook in a community of exceedingly well-to-do farmers whose homes, if not opulent even according to the standards of that day, were comfortable, well-ordered, highly provisioned, and offered to the world as firm an air of security, stability, competence, and contentment as it has ever known. Every house had its parlor properly Nottinghamed at the window, with Brussels or tapestry carpet on the floors, or ingrain at least. Will Carleton's poems reposed on the marble-topped tables along with the family album and a stereopticon. Rogers groups stood on a pedestal in many a bay window; whatnots held conch shells, little Staffordshire figures, and daguerreotypes; and in winter a fine and handsome chunk stove sent forth gracious heat and comfort even to the spare bedroom adjoining.

Cellars, "butt'ries," and storerooms almost burst with plenty, and huge barns, musky granaries, slatted corn-cribs, stone smokehouses, bulked large with food for man and beast.

Country dances, sociables, candy pulls, and parties of different kinds were frequent and gay, but the Shooting Club was somewhat exclusive and a little more opulent in its aspect than most of the social activities. The monthly excursions to the home of Uncle Matt and Aunt Martha, and from there to the Fowler farm where the shoot was held, were eagerly anticipated by all of us. We started in the morning and got to Uncle

Matt's in time for a one-o'clock dinner. The shoot began at three o'clock and the women went to the Fowler house to sew, visit, and prepare the supper.

My father, although urged to do so, did not enter into the sport of shooting. He was active and vigorous as ever, but with his usual pride in achievement he would not venture where he was doubtful of at least reasonable success, and he had never boasted unusual skill with any kind of gun. His hand, however, was steady, and with it he penned a handsome Spencerian script and made beautiful firm figures, so he was shortly made score keeper and there he would stand, stocky legs planted well apart, his feet encased in lumberman's felt-top boots drawn over his pants, a heavy "wam'us" over woolen shirt, an old coonskin cap on his head, pencil and score pad in his hand. His growing age was sitting well upon him, and in no way was that shrewd discerning mind affected by mounting years. He had, perhaps, mellowed a little, and while his bark had always been worse than his bite, there was now less violence in his protestations, less bluster to his assertions. There was, however, no diminution in his love of good food or any lowering of his standards in its preparation.

He was liked by older men for his keenness of wit, his bluff manner, and his sense of justice. He was respected by the younger men for his white hair, his rather austere manner, the keen penetrating glance from rather small, steel-blue eyes, and for the set of lips that never smiled upon a vulgar word or bawdy song. He was far from being a prudish man, but he was clean of mind and countenanced no filth. The women also held him a little in awe, simply because he was not one to encourage familiarity, and, like the women of his family, they hung upon his words and paid homage to what, by virtue of his silences, his air of dignity and pride, passed, perhaps, for more superior endowment than was justifiable.

My mother had and deserved a reputation for being an excellent cook, but there may have been a little something to the statement of the Covell youngster who quoted her mother as saying that my ma *had* to cook things good — because my pa 'd raise Cain if she did n't. He could still raise Cain if his salt-rising bread was not forthcoming three times a week, or if the fried-cakes from the iron "kittle" did not quite come up to the highest point of my mother's excellence.

She always contributed something to the Shooting Club supper, usually a cake, and also insisted upon helping in the kitchen whenever she was allowed. She loved a kitchen and liked to compare others with hers, and was invariably called upon at crucial moments or in the matter of seasoning. If she did happen to be out of the room when the oyster stew was all but ready for serving, or the dish of scalloped oysters ready to put in the oven, a call was sure to be sent out for her: "Oh, Miz' Thompson! Will you come out to the kitchen for just a minute? They want you to see if the 's salt enough — "

Her own contributions to the supper were hailed with admiration and praise.

"Shaw!" she would exclaim with ill-concealed pride. "What you make such a fuss for? They ain't a *bit* better 'n any one of you can make."

It was not, she protested, that her things were any better, but because, coming from someone outside the family, you thought they were. An argument, however true, that was forever refuted by her own household.

Sunset and dimming light drove the men from their sport. Some of those who lived nearest and had left no one to do the chores had to go home, returning as quickly as possible for the six-o'clock supper. Others helped the Fowler men with their chores and then repaired to washroom and a spare bedroom to change their thick boots for lighter ones, their heavy jackets for thinner coats.

The Fowler home was, of all the houses in that prosperous community, the largest, the most comfortably equipped. There was even a furnace in the cellar which, by means of sizable registers in the lower floor, sent up great waves of heat when fresh logs were thrown upon its fire, heat which found its further way to the second story by similar grilles in the ceilings. There was a piano in the parlor — this immediately establishing

a cultural superiority over most other homes in the
county, where only organs or at most a melodion accompanied the clustered voices when young people, and
older, met in groups on Sunday nights to sing.

More than this, the Fowlers had a billiard room —
of all unexpected appurtenances to a farm home! There
were six children in the Fowler family, four boys and
two girls, all between twelve and twenty-two. The
two oldest boys had attended school in Jackson and
there was talk of their going, another winter, to the
Agricultural College at Lansing. This year Mr. Fowler
was clearing a large timber lot and wanted their help.
Two younger boys and one girl were still in the city
school, being driven in on Monday morning and home
again on Friday. It would have simplified matters to
take them in on Sunday night, but they could not bear
to miss the gayety of the evening at home, so the two
older boys took turns in getting them in on Monday
in time for school. The youngest girl, twelve, was still
attending country school.

The billiard room was a recent adjunct to the house,
or rather a recent transposition of rooms. A large
bedroom, no longer especially needed as such since the
old grandmother's death in the previous spring, had been
stripped, painted, papered, and a new floor laid, the
entire work being done by the young people themselves,
and a billiard table installed.

"I need the boys this winter," Mr. Fowler told his

friends on the occasion of the first shoot of the season, when the billiard room was formally opened, "and I don't want 'em gadding off to town nights. It's *wuth* a few hunderd dollars to a man with boys to fix their home up so's it'll seem better to 'em than any other place." And it seemed a better place than any other not only to them, but to all the less fortunate youth of the community.

To this room, then, hastened the men, players and onlookers, with the small fry peering in at doors, underneath elbows, and around bulky backs.

My father stood in a doorway, rays from a hanging lamp over the centre of the table shining pinkly on his bald pate, his Greeley chin whiskers roundly and smoothly brushed, his hands in the pockets of his coat, his feet, encased in the cloth-topped, fine calfskin boots to which he had changed, squarely planted on the handsome floor.

He watched the game with kindling eye and slowly flushing cheek. It was a comparatively new game to all but young Danny Fowler, who had had some confessed experience in the city and was exhibiting a prowess which aroused not only the admiration of the spectators but his own. In fact he was getting quite cocky in the belief that not a man in the room was able to beat him.

Suddenly, to my own shocked horror and the apparent amazement of everyone else, my father, at the end of a game, stepped into the room, took a cue from the rack, and said, "Well, Danny, I'd like to see how this game goes. You show me?"

Graciously, if a bit condescendingly, Danny consented. Generously he gave my father the first shot. Not too clumsily my father balanced his cue upon the bridge of his left hand. Steadily he poised above it, his keen eye measuring distance and effect. Suddenly and sharply he hit the ball squarely in the middle. It caromed smartly against another and sank it into the pocket. He moved lightly to another point, bent with a sure grace over the table, let his eye mark the line from ball to pocket, and then there was the click, the roll, and another ball was home.

A little murmur of surprise came from the audience. Men leaned closer. Breaths were held. Young Danny, amazed that this old man, his fringe of silvery hair touching the velvet collar of his old black coat, with, presumably, no knowledge whatever of the game, should be proving a worthy opponent to *him*, spurred himself to the extent of his skill.

My father drove the balls as he might have driven a flock of unruly sheep to shelter. Young Danny began to hit wildly. Assaulted pride and embarrassment unsteadied his hand. When the last ball was driven home and my father turned to hang up his cue, Danny came around the table to say, "Well, Mr. Thompson, you sure showed me up. I bet that ain't the first time you ever played this game."

"Shaw!" said my father, modestly turning away. "I played it once or twice when I's a youngster."

On the way home Uncle Matt chuckled into the folds of his knitted scarf. "Didn't tell 'em you's the best doggone pool shooter in the county when you's a young feller, did you?"

"Shucks!" said my father diffidently. "I wasn't. It just come natural. And I ain't touched the thing in fifty years."

The pen that would picture to the eye that never saw, and can never hope to see, a table so bespread with lavish provender as was that set for an Oyster Supper at the Fowler farmhouse, the pen that would depict an old-fashioned oyster supper as once given by the Shooting Club in Southern Michigan, must justly poise in reflective mood above the waiting page. With what poor words shall it describe the fragrance, first of the opening cans, then of the heating broth as it steals through the kitchen door to anterooms, teasing the nose, aggravating to instant action the salivary responses of the tongue? How portray the long, wide table extending the length of the large dining room, duplicated by a second in the room beyond, each seating at least twelve people, the thick, satiny folds of their cloths hanging almost to the floor — for this was in the days when a housewife prided herself upon the size, quantity, and quality of her table linen.

In the centre of each table stood a stately silver caster
with cruets of sparkling glass, each bottle handsomely
etched and stoppered in heavy excellence of cut and
pattern. Flanking these were huge bowls of slaw, but
slaw of no common order such as housewives fling together with bowl and knife and a dash of salt and vinegar. This was slaw shredded to a hair and dressed with
thick sour cream, its own acerbity pitched to a little
higher key with vinegar ripened from the cider barrel,
the whole tempered by the dulcet quality of sugar and
savored with salt. No common slaw indeed, but a *cream*
of slaw, perfect accompaniment to oysters in any and
every form. Bowls of slaw, then, of palest green filmed
with cream and pointed with infinitesimal dots of black
and red pepper, bolstering the casters. And beyond
these at one end a high cylindrical glass dish holding
celery, and at the other one somewhat similar swinging
in its silver frame and filled with long spikes of cucumber pickles, slightly tart and strong of dill.

At each place was a large white china plate with gold
band around the edge, and threadlike circle of gold in
the centre. Silver flanked the sides: knife, soup spoon,
oyster fork, to the right; dessert fork, dinner fork, to
the left, and a goblet for water just above the plate
alongside a tiny butter dish — the same sometimes used
to hold the cup when tea or coffee was poured into the
saucer to cool. Mrs. Fowler's goblets were of the
thumb-print pattern, not so handsome as my mother's

bellflowers, but catching every reflected beam from the
hanging lamp overhead with its many prisms. The large
linen napkin, folded snugly square, lay at the left.

There was no food on the table other than the slaw,
the crackers, and the condiments, when we sat down,
except —

Except! Reposing on each dinner plate was a generous
saucer of oysters, raw. Not a cocktail glass, — we had
never heard of them, — but a saucer such as belonged to
a sizable cup. Oysters gray and cold, with tiny slivers
of ice here and there, releasing to the hungered nostril
a faint aroma recalling that first heavenly acquaintance with this succulent son of the sea as it was discovered to us in our own kitchen. Oysters to be dressed
according to individual taste or adventurous spirit, with
vinegar, horse-radish, ketchup from the casters, and salt
from the individual cellars before us.

These we ate with relish, and much laughter. The
spearing of a ketchup-drenched oyster on a small-sized
fork and its safe conveyance to the mouth was a sufficiently new enterprise to be undertaken with amusement. If there were any to whom the bivalve in its
natural condition did not appeal, the contents of their
dishes were more or less unobtrusively distributed among
those who could not get their fill.

This prelude to further delights disposed of, the
"ladies" replaced each saucer with a large deep plate
which sent up clouds of aromatic steam flavored of the

pots of Olympus, where gods once did their cooking and angels came to eat. Soup plates of a kind no longer known, but belonging to a day when soup was a goodly part of the meal, not merely a whet to appetite bored and dull. Soup plates filled with oyster *stew* made in a wash boiler. Made with milk that was half cream and brought to a boil but never boiled. Seasoned with salt and pepper, yellowed with butter, and the oysters dropped into it at the last moment to curl their fluted edges in its heat. Stew hot and tasty, and simply *gorgeous* to the tongue. But if you think that was all, you are wrong. The meal, you might justly say, is but begun.

When, after leisurely (and not too noisy) consummation of this overture to the real drama before us, the soup plates were gathered up and taken into the kitchen to be washed by the hired girl and the extra woman who had come in to help, great pans of scalloped oysters were brought in and placed at either end of the table — milk pans, shallow but large of girth, wrapped with snowy towels around their sides to hold the heat, disguise their plebeian nature, and make them easy to handle.

Down the table they were passed, down one side and up the other like a Virginia reel, the men holding the pan and politely helping their ladies before themselves. Oysters laid to bed with blankets underneath and above of crumbled crackers drenched with cream and butter. Oysters seasoned to a nice precision and done j-u-s-t to perfection, but not a jot or tittle either side.

My mother, now long versed in the art of cooking oysters in this manner to please my father's taste, usually had a hand in the preparation of these pans. "The secret," she told them, "of having *good* scalloped oysters is first in not having too deep a dish. If your dish is deep the oysters on top and bottom will be overdone, or those in the middle not done enough. And, next, in having just the right amount of milk, — which is half cream, — just the right seasoning of salt and black pepper, and plenty of butter. No scrimping on butter."

That is all there was (God save us! *All there was!*) to this course of the meal — just scalloped oysters, cream slaw, a dill pickle if you wanted it, celery, coffee, and quantities of hot, crisp, flaky riz biscuits and butter. Quantities of everything.

All there was, but — preceded probably by *two* huge plates of stew and the great saucer of raws — by cracky, it was enough, as my father vehemently remarked upon his introduction to this epicurean feast. Why they wanted to go, he scoffed after we had retired to Uncle Matt's house, and mess up such a taste as *that* in your mouth with *cake,* he could n't for the life of him see.

But there were those, nevertheless, and no inconsiderable number of them either, who liked their cake, and who looked forward to its appearance with as much eagerness as my father would to a piece of plum pudding after his Christmas dinner.

And with reason. My mother took no special pride in cake making other than in a certain spice cake which was a favorite with my father, and did not excel in the creation of those mountains of sweetness and beauty which were the joy of other women. Probably because, since ordinary cake and flimsy puddings were held in scornful disrepute by my father, she had never felt obliged to exercise what skill she may have had in their concoction.

With my Aunt Martha, however, with Miz' Fowler and Miz' Taylor, wife of one of the club members, as it had been with our old neighbor, Miz' Bouldry, cake making was an art. They made cakes as some paint pictures, weave tapestries, or create images in stone.

Aunt Martha, for instance, made, and frequently contributed to the supper, what she called the Black Queen's Cake, and while I have inherited my father's husky preference for vittles as against folderols and knick-knacks in cookery, I must admit that here was a cake worthy to follow even — if anything must follow — upon such a feast as this. Unfortunately I can find no record of her exact rule, but I did find, in a recent raid upon handed-down cookbooks and recipes in Southern Michigan, one that seems to approximate it in texture and flavor.

To perform the miracle, you put two cups of light brown sugar and half a cup of butter into a mixing bowl and cream these together. Add two unbeaten eggs and beat until light and fluffy. Put one level teaspoonful of soda into three fourths of a cup of sweet milk and add it to the above mixture. Then add two cups of flour, beating it in thoroughly, and two teaspoonfuls of vanilla.

Now put two and a half heaping tablespoonfuls of cocoa (or two and a half bars of chocolate melted) into a basin and pour over it one cup of boiling water, mixing thoroughly until dissolved. Add this to the cake mixture and stir well together. Pour into three well-greased layer-cake tins medium size, and bake thirty to forty minutes in a moderate oven. Do not bake too rapidly or too long.

When done, cool, and put together with the following filling: Take one half box of confectioners' sugar, cream with two tablespoonfuls of butter, and flavor with vanilla. Add two squares of bitter chocolate melted, or two table-spoonfuls of cocoa, and mix the whole with strong black coffee (very little at a time) to the right consistency, then beat until fluffy.

Now there is the Black Queen's Cake, and whatever African Majesty was deemed worthy of such homage must have been a queen indeed.

The cake for which Miz' Taylor held repute was known as a Watermelon Cake and for its colorful character was well adapted to its rôle as a major dessert. A rule guaranteed by one who in her youth knew my Aunt Martha, and who even in her ninetieth year still holds the yellow mixing bowl in a cunning hand, goes thus: "To make it," so says her time-stained page, "you take, for the white part, two cups of white sugar and one cup of butter and cream them together.

"Dissolve two teaspoonfuls of cream of tartar and one of soda in a little warm water and then mix it with a cup of sweet milk. Take three and a half cups of flour and mix alternately with the milk into the sugar and butter. Now beat up the whites of eight eggs to a stiff froth and add these last.

"For the red part, take one cup of red sugar and half a cup of butter and cream them together. Dissolve one teaspoonful of cream of tartar and one-half teaspoonful of soda in a little warm water and mix it with one-third cup of sweet milk. Beat the whites of four eggs stiff and stir them in. Now stir in one cup of lightly floured raisins.

"It requires two persons to fill the pan, which should be a large one with a tube in the centre, and well buttered. Keep the red part around the tube and the white part at the edge. This is a very attractive and ornamental cake."

And, one might add, a large and luscious one. Just to add the last note in such a symphonic scale in color, you might make a light green frosting, sort of mottled with white, and if you want anything more realistic the answer is to substitute watermelon for watermelon cake. The objection to our application of such substitution being that you could n't get watermelon and oysters at the same time — not in *our* country.

There were other cakes at other times: White Mountain cake; hickory-nut cake; whipped-cream cake; cup cakes frosted with red sugar — a very *plethora* of cakes, but the two I have given you were never far excelled in either taste or beauty of appearance, and always they were brought in in a manner suggesting Greeks and gifts, on glass cake dishes high and handsome.

What was done with all the "yelks" left over from these orgies with beaten whites I do not know, although I confess that every time I am admonished through these munificent old rules to "beat up eight whites," or ten whites, my poor, impoverished latter-day mind gives a sort of economical gasp. But they did not need to worry about a few egg "yelks," so why should I?

XI

Charivari

BIG JIM's wife, Adelaide, was my father's favorite niece, and her family was dear to him. To Adelaide "Uncle 'Lijer" was oracle and seer, and to him she came running a few weeks after we had moved to Millbrook, when their oldest son, William, — "Will-yum," his father called him, — got into a mess. At least that's what she called it — a mess.

"I wouldn't been surprised," she wailed, wiping her eyes on her apron (which she hadn't taken time to remove), "if it 'd been Gabey. Gabe's always doin' some fool-headed thing, but William — "

Just what, my father wanted to know, had William done? He also advised Adelaide to quit her bawlin' and act as if she 'd growed up.

"He 's got *married!*" Adelaide's voice rose to a hysterical wail, as she dropped into my mother's rocking-chair, her streaming face in her hands.

My father's mouth fell open. My mother, who was cutting friedcakes on a floury kitchen table, turned shocked eyes upon Adelaide.

"Married!" she echoed, sharply. "Who to?"

"That's *it*," moaned Adelaide, leaning forward to address them bleakly. "*Who* he's married!"

"Well, *who?*" My father was still speechless. My mother, floury hands leaning on the table, probed.

"It's a *woman!*" groaned Adelaide, covering her face again as if to shield her vision from some obnoxious sight.

"You act," observed my father tartly, "as if it was a walrus. Now stop actin' like a cow 'ts calf's been took away and tell what the trouble is." He did not sit down, preferring, apparently, to meet the situation standing. My mother set the kettle of smoking lard on the back of the stove and pulled forward a chair. Adelaide, a woman whom we had never seen robbed of a mild serenity which was her nature, had gained control of her emotions, smoothed her ruffled hair, and again wiped her face with her apron.

"Here," said my mother, proffering a handkerchief from a capacious pocket, "take this." Adelaide did, and then, swallowing the last of her discomposure, told the story.

It seemed that William, quite unbeknown to his parents, had been "carrying on" with a woman who had come to visit some relations of hers that lived four or five miles south.

"The Richardses," said Adelaide with contempt. "She's Miz' Richards's half sister from Detroit and they 've just been *after* William ever since she come. Worst of it is, Gabe 's known about it all the time. If he 'd a told us — " Her voice broke and, fearing a return of weeping, my father took a lid off the stove and fed the fire with a lavish hand.

"Told you *what?*" pressed my mother impatiently.

"Told us 't William was making a fool of himself over this woman — "

"When 'd he get married?" Practically, my father wanted facts.

"Yest'd'y. In Jackson. They stayed there all night."

"Where are they now?"

"They 're to home. They came out this morning. He had his horse and buggy. He 's been gone since Sunday." This was Tuesday.

Nobody spoke. The fire snapped. The stove lids grew red. The lard in the kettle on the back of the stove still smoked.

Finally my mother, her mind apparently on the mundane necessities of men, asked the question more vital to her mind than that of parental problems.

"Can she cook?"

"Goodness!" Adelaide, usually the most imperturbable of women, threw out her hands impatiently. "How in the world would *I* know? I never laid eyes on her before."

My father, with a stealthy movement, picked up his old felt hat from where he had hung it over the post of a chair. My mother's eye caught the action deftly.

"You better stay around awhile, 'Lije," she said. "Adelaide mebbe 'll want some help."

"Don't see what *I* can do," grumbled my father, twisting the greasy rim in his hands. "A man gets married, he's *married!*"

The statement was not challenged. He edged nearer the door.

"Gabey said — " Adelaide spoke tragically, as if the worst were yet to be revealed — " 't the boys are goin' to give 'em a hornin'."

My father stopped in his tracks. My mother sat upright. "You mean a — *shivaree?*" she demanded excitedly.

"Yes," Adelaide replied with an air of desperate admission. "Only Gabey said — he heard it over t' the blacksmith shop — 't it 'll be pretty wild."

My father hung his hat upon a nail near the door and came back into the room.

"What's the matter with the woman?" he demanded sharply.

"Well," said Adelaide miserably, "first place, she's a widder, but — her husband ain't — *dead!*"

My mother gasped and sat forward. "You mean — she — she's *divorced?*" The quality of scandalized dismay in her voice denoted her attitude toward the condition indicated.

Adelaide nodded. Her lip quivered. William was

her darling, her eldest. It was by no means *marriage,* even his marriage, before which she quailed. But that he had married *so,* a stranger, a woman whom he had not dared bring to his home beforehand for his parents' approval, according to the time-honored custom of country folk, but whom he had now thrust upon them, unknown, unwelcome, unwanted. A *divorced* woman.

My mother inquired the reason. People in those days did not divorce without good reason.

"Her husband was a drunkard, William says," Adelaide told her. "I don't hold with a woman puttin' up with drunkenness," she continued doubtfully, "not if he keeps it up. But a *divorce* — why, *she* could n't get no divorce for drunkenness."

No argument here. Drunkenness was not prevalent in our community, but in such rare cases as we knew of, women put up with it to the point of madness and finally either went home to their folks or did whatever else they could, but they did n't get a divorce.

"He must of done something terrible," opined my mother, but Adelaide only shook her head. "William says he did, but he did n't say what. He said if ever a woman had a right to get a divorce, she did."

"Pffh!" My mother's own particular expression of contempt engaged lips, tongue, and teeth, together with a lifted nose and backward toss of the head. "A woman can always pull the wool over a man's eyes if she gets him sorry for her. Specially a *young* man."

Adelaide nodded sadly. No doubt but that the wool had been pulled over William's eyes.

"What 's she *like?*" persisted my mother. My father still maintained his miserable silence. "How old is she?"

Adelaide's face fell, if possible, still further. "She 's older 'n Will-yum," she admitted bitterly. "Some. But she ain't bad-lookin', though. She 's kind of bold. She looks neat, but I would n't a wanted him to marry a widder — a *grass* widder — no matter *how* she looks."

"How 's Jim feel?" My mother cut in upon footless meditations.

"Jim never says *nothin'*." Those who knew Big Jim with his loose, gaunt frame, the deeply lined, big-nosed face, the half-smiling, half-grim mouth, could appreciate the statement. He talked but little, but what he said had purpose.

"He just said, 'Well, Will-yum, you better come along to the barn. We got to get ready for to-morrow.' You know we got thrashers," she interpolated. "We had to put 'em off on account of getting the new barn done. I wish't," she turned wistfully to my father, " 't you 'd come over to-night, Uncle 'Lijer — "

"What you want *me* over there for?" he demanded a bit testily. "I sh'd think you 'd got trouble enough."

"We have," Adelaide admitted sadly. "But I thought if the boys *did* come — "

"*I* tell you what we 'll do." My mother stood up

capably and smoothed her apron. "I 'll hurry my dinner out the way — it 's 'leven o'clock now — and finish my friedcakes, and then I 'll come over this afternoon and help you with the cookin'. 'Lije can come over to supper."

Adelaide's face brightened. "That 's right good of you, 'Miry," she said gratefully. "You bring Delly with you."

"Yes," said my mother. "She 's just getting over the measles and I ain't let her go back to school."

Neither of them consulted my father, but while the women stood talking at the open door he had slapped the old felt hat down over his bald head and escaped.

Far be it from me to question at this late day — and she long removed from the possibility of self-defense — any gesture of my mother's toward neighborliness or the obligations of kinship. Ever her ear was attuned to cry of distress, and always her feet were ready to turn toward a neighbor's need, her hands outspread to give of her service or her store. Quite as willingly would she have offered Adelaide the largess of her afternoon had there been no whet of her curiosity, but that desire to see this alien wife of the eldest son colored her eagerness is within the realm of reason.

Her name was Clara, and, in a child's estimation, she was likable and good. "Good," that is, as children rate character, in the way of kindliness to the young, the old, and the weak. Big Jim's mother lived with them, a woman of seventy or so, and at that time ill. Twenty times a day, in a figurative way of speaking, Clara ran to wait on her, picking up her knitting, placing a footstool, bringing her, as the day waned, a cup of tea, until she looked with growing favor upon her adored grandson's unwelcome choice.

Cory was ailing that day, too (too many friedcakes, my mother said), and Clara cut strings of paper dolls for her. She twisted paper into miraculously realistic roses and said that when her things came — if they *did* come; if, that is, she and William (she called him "Billy") were to stay there — she would get out some colored tissue paper and make *beautiful* flowers for us. Gran'ma Reed, less concerned at her age over morals than personal pleasure and comfort, told her *she* hoped she'd stay.

And Clara, it developed, had other accomplishments. From a pocket in the capacious folds of her alpaca dress (red, like a dark-hued hollyhock, trimmed with jet — her wedding dress) she whipped forth a jew's-harp and made gay, twanging music. A jew's-harp was nothing new, boys often had them; but no boy we had ever seen could command from one such a ferment and frothing of notes as came from the little instrument so firmly held between Clara's big white teeth, manipulated by Clara's brown, strong forefinger, the cadence controlled and measured by lips and tongue. It sounded like a thousand bumblebees droning musically, like a saw that had suddenly gone daft and taken to a musical breve as it cut through submissive wood. She stood facing Grandma and Cory, her back to the door. She smiled, too, as she played with mobile lips, her cheeks flushed, her eyes lit, her generously curved, wide-hipped body swaying a little in lilting unison with her tunes. "Arkansaw Traveler," she played, and the "Fishers' Hornpipe," and gentler tunes such as my mother sang — "Long, Long Ago," and "Nellie Gray." We were entranced. We stared at her, mouths agape.

Some sound, undefined, broke the spell. Simultaneously we turned. Adelaide and my mother stood in the doorway, their faces frozen into a perfect mask of amazement and, if later and more analytical judgment serves me, stern disapproval. "What!" they seemed to cry. "This interloper, this usurper, this destroyer of family peace and community welfare, daring to *enjoy* herself? And Gran'ma! Those children! Enjoying that heathenish music with her!"

Clara dropped the jew's-harp from her lips, wiped it with her hand, and buried it again in the folds of her dress.

" 'Scuse me," she said, dipping a little bow. "I thought maybe Gran'ma 'd like it." Grandma, smiling and nodding, had.

Their faces relaxed, resumed a more normal expression. Adelaide made heroic effort toward social poise. "You 're quite a musician, ain't you?" she observed, smiling thinly.

Clara beamed. Here, perhaps, was a port of entry into this harbor of family life from which she was as yet withheld.

"Yes," she said, eagerly, "but this ain't nothin'. I can play the 'cordeen, and the mouth organ. When my things come — "

"Mercy," cried Adelaide, turning suddenly and so thrusting my mother before her, "I smell something! I bet it's them cookies!"

That Clara was not of much assistance in the flurried preparations even a child could see, unless caring for and entertaining an old lady and a brace of little girls could be counted as assistance — which might or might not have been the case. Under usual conditions, Gran'ma Reed would have knitted, dozed, and maybe told a curdling tale of times when Indians unceremoniously clouded the kitchen door, and the little girls were quite accustomed to looking after themselves. Certainly nothing in the way of valuable contribution depended on Clara, but her small audience would have voted unanimously for continuance of her services. Moreover, no effort whatever was made on the part of those at the head of the household to draw her into their culinary activities.

Adelaide had an extra woman in to help — a woman from the village who, in this locality, performed that day-by-day service to the community that Miz' Lury

Lane, in our old neighborhood, had done for us. Her name was Mate Cooley, skinny, dour, and uncommunicative as Miz' Lury Lane was ample and loquacious.

With Cory shawled and pillowed on an old lounge (which in later years revealed its aristocratic lineage as a spool day bed of considerable value), her wistful eyes following Clara's every move, and Gran'ma Reed, also shawled against drafts and her feet in cloth shoes lifted to a small stool, comfortably dozing in her chair, I, being my father's daughter, found opportunity to make frequent incursions upon the kitchen.

Adelaide, Mate, and my mother, all veterans in the art of country cooking, moved from "butt'ry" to table to stove to table to "butt'ry," back and forth, forward and back, around and past each other like human shuttles weaving a pattern which had form, color, flavor, and a fourth quality, impalpable but memorably significant, that of odor. Odors piquant with spice as ginger-molasses cookies came from the oven, sheet after sheet, their fat bellies dented, navel-like, with a raisin plumped by heat. Odor of pumpkin being stewed down in an iron kettle, leafily sweet, its honest Western virtues awaiting miscegenation on the morrow with spices from the East. Odors presaging others still more poignant that would follow later: young lamb sizzling and roasting in the oven; hot, steaming, yeasty-smelling biscuits mysteriously veiled by snowy towels on the table; pungent tickle of freshly released relishes, spicily tart. All these and what others an initiated nose could safely prophesy flowed in fragrant drifts in and out of the more palpable pattern the women made in their ceaseless round. Apparently intent upon their immediate task, like solemn-minded spiders spinning their sinuous design with engrossed absorption, one nevertheless felt that beneath this seemingly diligent pursuit ran a breathless undercurrent of apprehension, anxiety, speculation, dread, and, in Adelaide's case, despair. When, as she infrequently did, Clara appeared in the kitchen for a drink of water, asking, hesitantly, for the makings of Gran'ma's tea, or a broom with which to sweep up her scraps of paper, every eye burned upon her like those of the jealous spider suspicious of alien foe. My mother spoke to her politely, but her eye did not light or her lips melt. Adelaide answered her questions, showed her the ways of the kitchen, but held aloof. William came in once during the afternoon, greeted my mother affectionately, eyed his mother wistfully — and suspiciously. Clara came to the door at the sound of his voice and stood, a half smile on her lips, a look of apprehension on her face.

"H'lo," he said, grinning protectively — and foolishly — at her. "How you makin' out?"

"All right," she answered, with forced courage, and he returned to his work.

After supper my father, who had appeared promptly at mealtime, and Big Jim went into the sitting room. Gabey, Philly, and Dan'l went out the door. Their dog,

a little white mongrel terrier, tagged along. Gran'ma
Reed had gone to bed, but Cory refused to go — and,
spoiled darling, was allowed to stay. Clara offered to help
with the dishes, but Mate would not have her. Adelaide
and my mother put away the food and then followed the
men. I was told to play paper dolls with Cory, but not
even paper dolls cut by the yard with hand clasping hand
— a newly acquired art — could quite deafen us to the
scraps of desultory conversation, mostly between my
mother and Adelaide. My father looked miserably uncomfortable. He had not wanted to come. He wanted
to go home, but my mother skillfully evaded his
pleading eyes. Big Jim joined him in unhappy silence.
Mate was still rattling and banging things in the
kitchen. William and Clara had gone upstairs, followed by William's dog, a red setter with silken droopy
ears.

" 'T ain't that I would n't of wanted him to get married," Adelaide said tearfully. "He 's twenty-one —
past. But I 'd always hoped he 'd marry one of the
girls around here — he 's been goin' with Jennie Myers
off and on for years, till lately."

"Yes," said my mother commiseratingly as Adelaide
paused, "you 'd a thought so. Still," her mind dealing
speculatively with the problem, "she looks capable — "

"Anyway," Adelaide straightened in her chair, shoved
the loops of chestnut hair back to reveal rather prominent
ears, and assumed her natural air of proficiency, "he 's

married to her.   He's made his bed.   Now he's got to
lay in it."

Big Jim's face lightened.   To have antagonized William,
now, with the belated threshing and fall ploughing before
them, would have been, to him, a major disaster.   Women
and family relations, dissensions, differences — these,
under sensible handling and with cool judgment, could in
time, he thought, be adjusted.   But fall work delayed for
want of help was irreparable.   All the available neighboring men were already engaged, and the time was too short
to go far afield.   More than that, however, he could not
bear the thought of alienating the affection or disrupting
the pleasant relationship between his eldest son and himself.   He, as well as Adelaide, had hoped, and expected,
that William would marry one of the neighborhood girls
and bring her home to live until such time as he could build
his own house.   He, as well as Adelaide, recoiled before
the thought of what was still a pariah in respectable
society — a divorced woman.   But as between accepting
William's choice and losing William there was no doubt.
All this was revealed, and plainly, even to the two small
girls playing so sedulously a fatuous game of paper dolls,
through the fitful words and scattered phrases that broke
the portentous silence.

It was dark outside by now, dark, with a fine cold mist
in the air that would turn to rain.   Talk grew more fragmentary.

"Well, 'Miry," my father shifted in the chair he had

tilted back against the wall, and looked hopefully at my mother. "Better be gettin' 'long home, think?"

Adelaide glanced nervously at the window, rose, and lowered the shade.

"Set a little spell longer, Uncle 'Lijer," she begged. " 'T ain't only half-past seven."

My father banged his chair down onto its four legs, leaned forward, and picked up a stick of kindling from the basket beside the round-bellied stove. He took his jackknife from his pocket, opened the blade, and began to whittle.

" 'Lijer!" Sharply my mother's voice stayed his restless hand. "For mercy's sake," she scolded, "don't muss up Adelaide's clean floor. Bad enough to have whittlin's all over the house to home."

"Clean dirt," muttered my father contentiously, but closed the knife and put it away, and threw the stick back into the basket.

The silence thickened. Even the commonplaces of relationship could not withstand the charged atmosphere of the room. I crept to my father's side and sat upon the basket of kindlings. He smoothed my hair, his rough warm fingers resting on my cheek.

"Where you s'pose the boys went?" Adelaide's voice was hushed. We were all haunted by the silence pressing itself against the veiled window, the closed door.

"Barn, prob'ly." Big Jim's lips opened merely to emit the words, and closed. The stillness prowled at the door, waited at the cracks, beat upon our hearts. Cory moaned. Adelaide, with one swift stride of her long firm legs, was at her side, cradling her, crooning.

Big Jim's deep-set dark eyes rested anxiously upon the little girl. Cory slept in her mother's arms.

My father's eyes pleaded. His bedtime hour had come. He had been working all day in the open. He drooped for want of sleep.

"Guess you might's well go home, 'Lije," rumbled Big Jim sympathetically, "if you want to. Don't believe the boys 'll cut up if they do come. Can't do nothing about it, anyway."

Adelaide raised her eyes fearfully. A charivari — "shivaree," as it was commonly called, or "hornin' " — was not always, as she well knew, a harmless pleasantry or neighborly form of serenade. Everything depended upon the spirit in which it was given, the attitude of the serenaders toward the groom and his bride. If the wedding pleased them, was satisfactory to them as a community affair, the din — for din it would be under any circumstances — would end in good-natured, if possibly boorish, raillery. The honored couple would appear at window or door, wave their appreciative greetings, and invite the "boys" in. Refreshments, either prepared in anticipatory expectation or part of the wedding feast, and cigars would be forthcoming, and the bride, initiated by bucolic wit and joke, often lacking in finesse and sometimes in good taste, into the freemasonry of wedded life, was accepted as one of themselves, and the party took itself off with the equivalent of blessings on the newly wedded pair.

On the other hand, one regrets to state, these expressions of neighborhood feeling toward the matrimonial transactions of their young were not always given in this commendatory spirit. Instances had been known where, with an implication of ribald contempt, the groom had been dragged from his nuptial bed and forcibly detained therefrom the entire night or longer, while horns tooted, kettles were beaten, guns shot off underneath the window of the frightened bride; where, though these were exceptional cases, the disorderly farrago, incited by the fillip of hard cider, had grown to a riot and injury had been done.

And as sure as the fate that Adelaide — and Big Jim no less — felt was drawing in upon them, this wedding would meet with no tender handling.

Billy Reed had been a favorite in his neighborhood. Indeed, he had been one of the most popular boys in the whole county. But he had transgressed every code of country custom. He had gone steadily with one girl and then suddenly gone off and married another. He had married secretly, thus denying his friends a fanfare of such merit as offspring of Adelaide and Big Jim should provide. And, worse than all, he had married a "grass widder"! No man in all their acquaintance had ever married a "grass widder." In fact, a divorced woman was so little known to our community that judgment was based entirely upon prejudice. When people got married they stayed married. Literally they took each other for better, for worse. If it turned out worse, why, as Adelaide said of her own son, "He's made his bed, now let him lay on it."

Before he could begin "laying" on it in earnest, however, he had to deal with social justice as meted out by his contemporaries. In general, country marriages turned out fairly well. Not too much was expected of them, nothing startling came of them. But golden weddings were not unknown.

Suddenly, not so much the sound as the premonition of sound crept upon our strained and listening ears. Out of some remote and echoless distance came the slow rumble of wheels on hard earth, heavy iron-rimmed wheels rolling smoothly over the sandy road to the blunt slow rhythm of horses' feet.

Faces were lifted. Eye met eye. The men's figures tensed. Adelaide paled. She laid Cory back upon the lounge unwaking, covered her, and stood, rigid and alert.

The door from kitchen to woodshed opened with a jerk and the three boys came striding in, but on feet as silent as their cowhide boots would allow. The little white dog, with nervously cocked ears, followed.

"*They're comin'!*" Hoarsely, on expelled breath, twenty-year-old Gabey, as spokesman, gave the warning.

"S-s-s-s-h!" Adelaide, with finger on lips, indicated the sleeping child, who moved and slightly moaned.

"Set down." She indicated chairs, and the boys sat. "Don't nobody say a word." She drew her own low rocking-chair close to the couch and sat, brooding over the little girl. I, frightened, but terribly excited, crept close to my father's knee.

The roll of wheels, the heavy, thudding clump of horses' feet, drew nearer, but stopped some little distance down the road. Then came voices — low, muted, deep. Laughter, quickly hushed. The little dog barked and was swiftly muzzled. From upstairs, in William's room, came an answering bark, instantly hushed. A clatter followed, as of motley wares clashing. A curse. Footsteps approached. My mother, unable further to endure inaction, crept to the window, knelt, and peered under the shade.

"Can't see a thing," she whispered. " 'S dark as pitch."

Suddenly, however, with a rending blare the silence was ripped into a thousand shreds of shattered, stunning, obscene noise. My father and Big Jim sprang to their feet. So did the boys. Cory woke with a cry and Adelaide soothed her. My mother stuck to her post. Gran'ma Reed in nightgown and cap, with a gay plaid shawl around her shoulders, came to the stair door.

"What in Goshen 's the matter?" she cried.

"Go back to bed, Mother," Adelaide told her. " 'T ain't

nothin' but the boys serenadin' Bill." She went back.

William came clattering down the stairs. Adelaide held up her hand. The mildest of women, she fiercely dominated the room. "Hush!" she commanded. "Don't you *move!* Any of you!"

William, halfway to the outer door, paused. "You think I 'm goin' to stand here and let them sons — "

Adelaide rose and stood, tall, big, rigid, her face ashen through its tan, her dark eyes burning.

"You men keep out of this," she commanded. There was no need of lowered voices now. Nothing could be heard above the outside din. "You 'd only make a mess of it and get into a fight — "

"A *lickin 's* what they 're goin' to get," Big Jim broke in, his face like an ugly iron mask. "You think we 're goin' to — "

The noise grew worse. Cowbells, tin horns, metal upon metal (iron rods upon a wagon tire, we later learned), pounded dishpans, the crack of a rifle — and now voices.

"Hi, Bill! Fetch out the widder!"

"Come on out, Bill. Le 's see the gal. She orter be a good 'un. Had practice!" Guffaws of laughter, raucous, caustic, mingled with the racket.

William, with a muttered curse, strode toward the door, Big Jim beside him. My father was moving unnoticed toward the kitchen. Adelaide sprang to the door, turned her back upon it, and faced her men.

"Keep back!" she cried. "All of you! Uncle 'Lijer, where you goin'?"

"Well," said my father with suspicious mildness, "I thought a good big pail of water in their faces — "

"You come here!" Meekly my father returned and stood, like a guilty boy, awaiting orders.

"Now," said Adelaide, covering them, husky men and gawky lads, with a dominating eye, "I want you should stay right here. Don't you make a move. Not *one* of you. *I'm* going out there — "

"*No!*" thundered William, striding toward her.

"*Yes!*" said Adelaide, fending him off motionlessly. The din grew nearer. They were close to the steps. They were shouting to Bill to come out.

"We're comin' to fetch you, Bill," they threatened. "If you want to git your pants on, ye better hurry."

"Need n't bother to dress the widder," and other vulgarities, followed. Horns blared. Cowbells clanged. Pans rattled. Rifle shots ripped the mist. Bedlam roared.

William tried to thrust his mother aside, but she held her ground.

"Hand me that lamp!" Adelaide reached out a hand, and Big Jim obeyed. "Now stand back — out of sight." The men fell back.

With the lamp in her hand, held high, Adelaide flung wide the door and stepped out upon the stoop. From our sheltered darkness we could see darker indistinct figures, wet faces under slouched hats, hostile eyes, pencil gleams of light on metal. With Adelaide's appearance the din lessened.

"G'd evenin', boys," she called, her voice threading the heavy mist vigorously. "If you 'll quit that racket a minute I want to say something to you." Horns were lowered, bells, tires, and pans subsided. Every man among them knew Bill's mother and respected her. Moreover, they had eaten at her table, many of them, since their childhood, and obligations of hospitality sat heavily upon them. Some of them had worked with and for Big Jim, and would to-morrow, and Big Jim was a man of standing, as well as a man of brawn. Their wives, sisters, and mothers, many of them, were lifelong friends of Adelaide's.

"I see," said Adelaide, moving the lamp to and fro above her head, where its yellow rays washed across familiar faces, "the 's a good many of Bill's old friends amongst you, so I take it you 've come to celebrate Bill's gettin' married."

Forms shifted in the dark. Feet shuffled. Throats made futile, foolish sounds. A voice from the rear shouted, "Tell *Bill* to come out. We want to see Bill!"

"You listen to *me* for a minute." Adelaide lowered the lamp to where it illuminated her own face, austere, stern. "We 'd all be glad to have you come to see Bill — and Bill's wife." A little narrowing of the eyes accompanied this challenge. "But, you see, this is *my* house you 've come to, mine and Jim Reed's, and I don't just exactly like the way you 've gone at it." A shifting of the lamp so that faces on the outer edge of the group were suddenly revealed was met by embarrassed shuffling of feet.

"I s'pose you *meant* well," she went on discursively, "because none of William's friends — or ours — 'd mean anything else." Furtive exchange of glances, sheepish grins, acknowledged the finesse of this move. "But I don't think you see this matter the way *we* do, and I want you should before you do any more serenadin'. Now — William 's married. And he 's brought his wife here — to home. Maybe he ain't married just the one we 'd a picked out, and maybe after we get to know her we 'd a picked her out from everybody else. Anyway, the point is — he 's married. It 's his choice, and he 's got a right to make it. He 's brought her home and *she 's goin' to be a member of this neighborhood.* Now the time may come when William 'll wish he had n't of married her. Mebbe the time 's come when some of you older fellers" (the lamplight washed over faces upon which Adelaide's knowing eye ironically dwelt) "wisht you had n't of married the women *you* did! But you can't *do* anything about it — now. And Bill can't, neither. Gettin' married is — *gettin' married.* It 's *set.* Like plaster.

"You fellers — the way you've come here, makin' a racket fit to raise the dead — look to me as if you don't *like* the way Bill's got married. I ain't goin' to say it's none of your business, because it is. Bill's one of you. Born and raised amongst you. Anything he does *is* your business. Just as what you do is his. You've stood by each other in lots of things. Now, if you think Bill's done something he's going to be sorry for, *this* ain't no way to show it. Nor no way to help *him*. I think mebbe you're mistaken. *I* think this girl's goin' to work in all right. She's had some hard luck. But that's all the more reason for you boys that *ain't* had no hard luck not to behave yourselves this way.

"Now I tell you what I want. I want you boys should go home. If you want to see Bill *he'll* see you all right. I practically had to tie him up to keep him inside. But I *don't* want you to see his wife — her name's Clara. Rather, I don't want her to see *you* — to-night, lookin' way *you* do — like a lot o' hoodlums. I'd be ashamed of you, same's I would *my* boys if they's out there.

"And I tell you what more I'd like. I'd like all of you, the hull kit and caboodle of you, to come over, and give Bill and Clara a reg'lar home-comin' party. And fetch your wives. And your sisters — and girls. None of this night-owl-hootin'-around-alone stuff. Come to supper and show our — our new daughter that she's come into a real decent neighborhood — not a monkey cage. I'll let you know when — just as soon's we c'n get this

thrashin' out the way and the fall work. We 're terrible
late with it and I can't do nothin' till we 're through and
we get the house straightened. Then I want you sh'd
come. We 'll have a dance. What say — you do that?"

A chorus of "Sures" — "*Bet* we will" — "Good for
you, Miz' Reed" met her challenge as they milled and
shifted.

Adelaide turned to the door. "Here," she called.
"Come out here, William."

William came out, grinning, looking unspeakably foolish, and stood beside her. The crowd yelled, shouted.
"Hi, Bill!" "Go it, Bill!" "Good luck, Bill." "See
you later, Bill." "Put one over on us, did n't you,
smarty?" But it was good-natured raillery now, and
they were turning away. Bill waved his hand.

"Go on home, you damn fools," he shouted at them,
grinning. "What I ought to 've done 's to come out here
and lick the hell out of you. Would, too, if Ma 'd let
me. She 's too darned good to you."

They howled and laughed. Jeered at him, but happily. He was their old Bill again and they would support him to a man, whatever matrimonial *faux pas* he
might have committed.

Big Jim and the three younger boys joined Adelaide
and Bill. The straggling little band of subjugated serenaders squashed through wet grass and mud to their
wagon. It was raining now.

"Fetch a fiddle when you come," shouted Big Jim, as

we heard them clambering into the wagon, the horses starting, "and leave that dod-burned junk to home." A final blast from horns, a last clatter of cowbells, a clash of pot covers, a good-humored "Good luck, Bill" — and the shivaree was over.

XII

Country Dance

F-i-r-s-t, lady and gent swing into the middle,
Bal-ance the floor and keep time with the fiddle;
T-h-e-n, *back* to your place and swing once around,
La-dy in centre, and *seven* hands round.

EITHER there had not been much dancing in the neighborhood where we lived before moving to Millbrook, or else we had not heard of it. This might very well have been the case since my father was, from earliest remembrance, far past any dancing years he might ever have had, and was, moreover, openly opposed to such "cutting up and capering" as would deprive him of an early bed.

Neither was my mother of the capering kind, and so there may have been dancing all around us and we none the wiser, except that if there had been we should almost certainly have known it through the Covells, who, shiftless, slothful, improvident though they were, never missed any kind of social function, especially where food was part of the entertainment. And since nothing of the nature of a country dance was ever reported by them,

either by the girls, with whom I often played, or by their
parents, who came frequently to our house to borrow, if
for no other reason, it is safe to assume that ours was a
staid community where heels and toes were put only to
legitimate use.   Church Sociables, Sunday School picnics,
Strawberry Festivals — these were yearly and seasonal
diversions, but it was not until we moved to Millbrook
that we became acquainted with the Country Dance; and
even then, as part of a community's social life, our active participancy in such festivity was limited.   Not, by
any means, that a child of ten or even younger would
have been a hindrance, for people took their children,
even babes in arms, to the country dance.   Infants were
laid to sleep on the spare bed along with overcoats, nubias,
fascinators, hoods, scarves, and mittens, while older children cluttered the floor until they fell asleep and were
likewise cradled.   Not, indeed, from any parental vigi-
lance, but because my father was n't going to be dragged,
cajoled, coerced, or otherwise led into what he termed
the "biggest tarnation fool way of spending a man's bedtime hours anybody could think of."

What! — thus he delivered himself when Adelaide
and Big Jim insisted on his coming to the dance late in
November which was to be a home-coming party for
William and Clara (particularly Clara, since William
was already at home).   What!   *He,* a man of *his* age,
to go caperin' off over there to see a lot of old coots and
young fools prancin' around on the floor, kickin' up their

heels like colts in a windstorm?   He guessed not!   Moreover, he was n't goin' to start takin' *Delly* out to no such
shindigs.   First thing *he* knew she 'd be wantin' to go
gallivantin' off by herself.   And much more in the same
strain.

But Adelaide *was* his favorite niece, and when she came
blandishing her "Uncle 'Lijer" with soft words and the
plea that this was their first big "company" since the
new house was built, and that it was a welcome to Clara,
and William's feelings would be hurt if Uncle 'Lijer
was n't there, though the argument met with character-
istic bluster, the day was won.   Especially when she told
him that Stib Obart was coming to fiddle and call off.
Big Jim had told the boys to fetch along a fiddle, but
Adelaide, once she had put her heart into a real housewarming for the new home as well as a tribute to William's wife, would brook no ordinary measures.   So
Gabey had been sent off to engage Stib Obart, with Abe
Morton as second fiddle and Ranse Miller's guitar to
support him.

It may be remembered that Stib Obart's pliable fingers,
which could bring sudden and violent death to a porcine
throat quicker than any other man's in the county, could
also so seduce the neck of a fiddle as to bring forth both
the tricksy lilt of jig and rigadoon, and the more seduc-
tive strains of the simple waltz.

My father had seen Stib Obart butcher hogs a good
many times, but he had never heard him play the fiddle

for a dance, so when my mother began to get herself in readiness for the party, my father also made his preparations. Not with any show of eagerness, of course, but as an abused and down-trodden victim of feminine whim. My mother, however, went ahead with her toilet, ignoring both the petulant irascibility with which he scrubbed, lathered, shaved, trimmed, and brushed, and the succeeding air of pathos which increased as he became more and more the object of his own compassion.

From our house to Big Jim's was less than a mile. They lived just beyond the turn at the west end of Main Street and we on a crossroad at the other, and so my father thought to hitch up a horse for such a trifling distance a matter of utmost folly, but my mother was adamant. She and I had on our best clothes. To be sure, our cloth-top shoes were protected by arctics and our good dresses by winter coats. Nevertheless, there had been a fresh and heavy fall of snow and she wasn't going to have the bottoms of our skirts wet and draggled when we got there. Besides: —

"Don't tell me you're goin' to wear them old cowhide boots, 'Lije Thompson," she stormed as he shucked himself into the shabby seam-worn overcoat that had covered his thick stooping shoulders ever since I could remember.

My father looked down at his boots, plainly amazed.

"What's the matter 'th these?" he demanded contentiously. "*I* ain't goin' to dance."

"Well," my mother told him smartly, "mebbe you ain't. But you ain't goin' to wear them old barn boots to Adelaide's, either. They *stink*. You go 'long and change 'em."

So he took the bootjack out from behind the stove, sat down and hauled off the offending brogues, changing to the fine, hand-stitched calfskin boots with long cloth tops that had stood him for best in footwear even longer than the old overcoat had protected him in winter.

Then he lit the lantern, grumbling a little about such "tarnation foolishness, makin' a man gallivant off after dark when he ought to be gettin' into bed," and went out to hitch up the horse.

He said little more, but as we took our places in the low, square-boxed pung and drew the robes around us, he expressed himself briefly: "I ain't goin' to *stay* over there," he warned us. "Soon 's you 've had your fling I 'm goin' to hitch up and come home."

My mother laughed. "I don't want to stay myself," she said, agreeably. "We 'll stay a little while and then come home."

Not even the frost-sweet air of a star-spangled, snow-white winter's night, however, its silence broken into a thousand silver echoes by the string of tiny bells encircling the old horse's rounded belly, could lift my father from the slough of dejection in which he was submerged. And so in silence — save for the pleasant crunch of runners on the snow, the rhythmic thud of the horse's hoofs, and the tintinnabulation of the bells — we proceeded on the rime-bound road to Adelaide's.

Adelaide greeted us at the door. Adelaide in a new merino dress of brown — the gold brown of a hazelnut fresh from its deeper sheath. A dress all trimmed with narrow golden braid and golden buttons down the front, with a bit of ruching at neck and wrists and a gold brooch at the throat. Adelaide with her chestnut hair combed smoothly down each side of her wide, pleasant face in a heavy loop over her ears to join the roll at the back of her head. Adelaide smiling and greeting: —

"Where 's Uncle 'Lijer? Philly," to one of the four grinning awkward boys flanking her on either side, "you go help Uncle 'Lijer with the horse." And Big Jim looming behind her, his heavy black hair awry, the cowlick at his crown contrarily askew, looking red and proud and foolish, all dressed up and happily uncomfortable in his best clothes, with Cory, "pindlin' " and white, clinging to his hand.

Beside William, canting a little toward him, stood Clara. Clara in her red wedding dress with its tight basque swelling at the bottom over plump hips and closely buttoned over full-blossomed bosom, with rows of sparkling jet. Clara, whose frizzy hair betrayed the use of curling irons and to whose flushed cheeks a perfumed powder clung — a toilet accessory not as yet considered an essential to a woman's costuming, and by the use of which Clara's status in the community was at once resolved.

So Clara stood at William's side widely smiling and showing teeth of extraordinary perfection and brilliance. Clara bowing, shaking hands, saying "Please' to meet cha," but with an unease in her manner, a questioning doubt in her eye on which my mother later remarked. "Scared 't folks ain't goin' to take to her," she said after we had got home and were in the process of retirement. "William looked a little worried too."

"Huh!" my father adjoined sleepily. "Ought a done his worryin' earlier."

Our wraps laid away on the spare bed with those of the few earlier guests who had preceded us, we were ushered into the sitting room, reserved for those who did not dance, and joined our neighbors. It was a pleasant room — or so it seems to me now. There was a rag carpet on the floor — gay stripes of red and brown and green with alternate ones of hit or miss set off with black. There was a whatnot in one corner on which were curious things — a chunk of ore, souvenir of the gold rush to which Big Jim's father had contributed his presence and from which he had brought this and other specimens distributed among friends. You could actually *see* the gold in the rock. An ostrich egg from God knows where, dried and rattling. A candy apple with pale green realistic leaves, licked surreptitiously by Cory until the flesh was gone from its cheeks. A gray stone pig which, uncorked, would give forth ketchup in a most unsightly manner, and other treasures similar to, but different in character from, those found on whatnots in most neighboring homes.

A row of women sat on the lounge along one wall, a group of men opposite. The two were as uncommunicative with each other as if they had never met. Cory and I stole quietly to vantage points here and there.

My father came in, looking a shade less morose, joined the men, and they talked. Others arrived, stamped the snow from their feet, and joined us. Big Jim threw a fresh chunk into the round stove and the room became hot. The smell of woolen garments mingled with that of food from the kitchen — baked ham, pickles, hot biscuits, cake.

Suddenly there was a commotion at the door. "It's the music!" The word went round. "The music's come." We all stared, and "sure as you're alive and livin'," Stib Obart strode through the room, his fiddle in its wooden case under his arm, his long thin figure leaning a little forward as if pushed by some invisible wind, his hawklike face, led by its hatchet beak, turning neither right nor left. On his face the same intent, absorbed look that we had seen as he marched upon the scene of slaughter, the deadly dirk sheathed in its homemade leathern pouch.

"The music's here." The "music" was apparently

centred upon the Lincolnesque figure of Stib Obart, since the second fiddle and guitar were already present and waiting.

"We got good music to-night," remarked Adelaide complacently. "We thought seein' it 's the first party we ever had, we 'd do it up brown."

From the parlor issued sounds new to the ears of a little girl who had never even seen a dance, but strangely titillating to her small feet. The music was tuning up! The first fiddle, tenderly cradled in Stib's thin scrawny neck, plaintively squalled "A-a-a-a-a-a," followed by the reflexed echo of the second, while Ranse Miller's stubby farmer fingers plied the keys of his guitar and brought the slipping strings up to a pitch of harmony, according to the book of instructions supplied by the mail-order house from which he bought the instrument.

I edged around between the forest of legs and arms crowded about the door as only a thin and curious child can do, and the room came into view.

Now the usual custom in a farming community such as ours was to remove all the furniture from the room in which the dancing was to take place, take up the carpet, remove the straw, and scrub the floor. For, as you may know, all good farmers' wives put fresh clean straw under their rag carpets at housecleaning time in the fall. A little later, when newspapers became more plentiful, these were hoarded throughout the year and substituted for the straw, but in Adelaide's time, — and locality, —

straw was the medium used for warmth and cushioning effect.

Adelaide, however, had not yet bought any furnishings for the parlor of her new house, but had used it as a storage place for the barrels of brown and white sugar, crackers and salt, the sacks of coffee, and other groceries with which Big Jim provided her. Therefore there had been nothing to do but remove these to kitchen, pantry, and woodshed, and clean the floor.

In the farthest corner of this room near a window were three chairs for the "music." That is, the second fiddle and guitar occupied two chairs, with a third waiting for Stib Obart when he had exhausted himself, as he was bound, in time, to do. For even though the pursuit of butchering was only an occasional and, actually, a seasonal profession, Stib, at other times, followed the agricultural calling and made a tidy living off his small farm. Therefore, after a day in the fields, woods, or barn, this business of stepping, swaying, bending, shouting, swinging, dancing, with those whose feet knew rhythm, and fairly carrying the plodders upon his own back, to say nothing of the mental strain of setting his calls to rhyme as he went along, was bound to wear a man down.

Now, however, he stood, alert, waiting. Dressed in a long black coat, ancient as the airs he played and reflecting the light from the lamp above along its seams and back, with a white shirt and celluloid collar, and small black tie secured by a loop to the collar button in front, he stood, and called: —

"S'leck your pardners for a kadrille!"

The floor was quickly filled. The fiddles sawed a little to see that no strings had slipped — the dance was on.

William and Clara stood at the far end of the room and were the "head couple," Gabey and Sadie Dickson, the miller's daughter, at the right. Ed and Freda Calkins (Ed was the druggist) were on their left. I do not remember who was at the foot.

"S'lute pardners!"

They bowed; the men scraped, as properly taught, with the right foot a little to the rear, circling a little to the left, toes pointing stiffly down. The women curtsied with what grace was natural or acquired.

The dance progressed.

> F-i-r-s-t — four — *lead* to the right.
> Swing 'em around with *all* your might!
> Back to your places and *swing* 'em around —
> Lady in centre and *seven* hands round.

Feet shuffled. Dust rose. Heat mounted. In a pause between figures someone raised a window. The sweet cold air rushed in. Men frankly mopped their faces with huge handkerchiefs. The girls fanned themselves with fans suspended from their wrists. Clara danced a little differently from the others. I should not then have known how to describe it. Now I would let it go as *abandon*. The other girls did not give themselves to the dance — Clara did. Ed Calkins swung her until she squealed and staggered a little when he flung her into place. William did not look pleased.

The dancers stood at ease waiting for the next figure. The door was filled with onlookers. A few were seated in chairs close to the wall. The fiddles were tested: A-a-a-a-a-a — *A-a-a-a-a-a.*

Ranse Miller turned the keys of his guitar, plunked chords. The tune changed: —

> *All* join hands and circle to the left.
> Stop right there and *grand* right and left —
> *Back* to your places, and *swing* 'em around;
> Gent in the centre and *seven* hands round.

The sweat poured off Stib Obart's face. It ran down into the handkerchief that swaddled the neck of the fiddle. He mopped his face with this and took a fresh one from a pocket in the tail of his coat to thrust beneath his jaw. This business of seeing four couples through the intricate figures of a quadrille was far more exhausting than butchering half a dozen hogs. He shouted his calls so they could be heard at the next house — if not too far away. He stepped with the music, describing the base of the triangle formed by the corner where the music sat. He took the fiddle from underneath his chin and swung it over his head. He sang his calls, often making up his rhymes as he went. The managerial air dropped away. He became frolicsome.

> *Head* couple swing with the couple on the right.
> (*Hi*, there, Dan, don't hold 'er so tight!)
> Pass to the next and *all* face about —
> Three hands 'round and *leave Dan out!*

A schottische followed the quadrille in which only a few took part, while those who had romped through the last measure of the "square dance" caught their breath — and probably a cold, standing in open windows or rushing, half-dressed, as the older women said (long-sleeved and long-legged underwear, corset covers, drawers, petticoats, and wool or possibly silk dresses, high necks, wrist-length sleeves), out onto the stoop to cool off.

After this a waltz — *tee*-dee-dee, *tee*-dee-dee, tee-*dee*-dee-dee! A nice, rhythmic measure, with a steady pulsing beat to it that took you round and round the room — *one*, two, three, *one*, two, three, *whirl* half around; *one*, two, three, *one*, two, three. None of your silly new-fangled slip here, slide there — and nobody knows where you 're going.

As the first slow, throbbing notes crept through the rooms William went to where Jennie Myers was sitting with some other girls and made his stilted bow. He murmured stilted words and she got up and went with him to the other room.

Cory and I were thrilled. It was a strange thing — and sweet — to see them go around and around that way, slowly, not very close together, their bodies hardly touching, William's one hand supporting Jennie's back, the other clasped in Jennie's — lifted high. They did not speak. They looked very solemn. I thought Jennie looked as if she might cry. William's face was set and stern. When the waltz was over they walked back to where she had been sitting, he bowed and left her, and went out of doors to where some of the other men and boys were standing.

Clara danced continually. She was very popular. Her face grew red and the powder was gone.

A second quadrille was called and the "set" was filled. Stib Obart had had time to cool off. Just *bend*-ing here, *nod*-ding there, *sway*-ing right and left, to the measured tune of the waltz, was merely a rest period for a man of his ardor and zeal. Moreover, he gathered dash and vigor as the evening progressed. As a general thing Stib Obart was a silent man — "loony," my father said, "as any man must be whose main job was hog killin' with fiddlin' for dances to offset it." He used hardly to speak even at table when he came to our house, "butcherin' time," eating his food rather daintily, finishing his business, and departing in moody silence.

Even at the country dances where his more artistic services were in demand, he never visited between dances as the other musicians did. He would go out on the stoop to smoke a pipe or eat an apple, and return to his stand, long-jowled, his sandy moustache mournfully drooping, his lacklustre eyes following his long nose to the chair whereon the fiddle lay.

Once in action, however, Stib Obart became a figure foreign to his seemingly natural self. It was as if a torch had been applied to some inner flame. His bony form lifted, strengthened. His eye brightened. The sandy tufts of hair above his eyes bristled. With a thrust of his long fingers through his saffron hair he would send the cowlick rioting a dozen ways, one lock cocked at right angles to his head, another straggling down over his eyes. With one dynamic shucking together of his joints and muscles, like a train of freight cars bumped by a coupling engine, he would spring as if to attention before the dancers. With a flourish encompassing a radius the length of his long arm he would saw a few exploratory notes, and then shout, as a call to arms: —

"S'lute pardners — and *bal*ance all!" Like the flash of a robin's wing to branch, the fiddle would home to its position underneath his jaw. Then, with a sway of his long body that described at least a quarter of a circle, his every nerve, fibre, and joint in perfect harmony with the tune he was playing, the old bow sweeping up and down and round and back and in and out, Stib Obart, the "loony hog killer," would pipe the stout-fisted, stout-hearted farmer folk before him away from their every-day lives to one of sheer motion and sound.

Not that any great amount of stimulus was needed to set heels and toes, however clumsily clad, to nimble play. Stib Obart called his figures, and men and women forgot the heavy tasks of to-day, the menial labor of to-morrow, and were joyously lost in relaxed nerves, unflexed muscles, and a mind voided of all save mere sensuous pleasure in rhythmic sound and bodily response.

Teetering bodies on itching feet. (*Oh, my goodness,*

ain't she sweet.) Heel and toe and away we go! (*Tune up the fiddle and rosin up the bow*.) Cuttin' a pigeon wing on the side. (*I laughed to myself till I almost died!*)

Now the "Irish Washerwoman" went racketing, clattering, tittering, doodling, caroling, chirruping, twittering, quavering, beating the air with a lilt and a song until even my father's obstinate foot joined the tattoo upon the dusty floors.

> F-i-r-s-t — *couple* swing out, and into the middle
> And *shake* your feet to the tune of the fiddle,
> Then, ge-*ents* swing out and the ladies swing in —
> All join hands and go it ag'in.

"Money Musk" and the "Opera Reel" alternated with "Pop Goes the Weasel" and "The Girl I Left Behind Me."

My father's eyes grew heavy, his brisk beard drooped. His feet no longer tapped. He wanted to go home.

"Time Delly was to home and in bed." He stood in the kitchen door and mumbled to my mother, where she was helping Adelaide. I was ready to agree with him. But supper was about to be served. It was called a "lap supper." That is, the supper was arranged on plates in the kitchen, and passed. Each man sought the lady he brought and sat beside her.

This was going to be a good supper, as I knew, for Cory and I, between enraptured observance of the dance, had paid respectful and mouth-watering attention to its assembling.

Pans of raised biscuits, hot and steaming as they were

partly split to admit generous collops of butter; a kettle of diced potato simmering in cream and yellow with butter; a loaf of meat — veal and pork, for the like of which, though it may not be the same, I found, while on a recent visit to Michigan, a rule dug out of an old cookbook contemporary with those days.

Also on the stove was a huge coffeepot which emanated an odor mysteriously tantalizing to the yet inexperienced palate of one small girl, but apparently within the acquaintance of the other.

"My," whispered twelve-year-old Cory, smacking her pale lips, "that coffee smells good!" Whereupon it developed that Cory had breakfasted on coffee, heavily sweetened and thickly creamed, as long as she could remember.

"Yes, and look at her!" replied my mother indignantly when Cory's greater privileges were reported to her ear. "Ain't got enough blood in her to look red when she's cut."

Others agreed with Cory, however, that the coffee smelled good, my mother among them, as the cover was lifted to admit a partly beaten egg, shell and all, to settle it.

"Makes me hungrier 'n all get-out," said my mother, sniffing. "Seems 's if I never smelt anything so good in my life. It's a wonder," she added to Adelaide as they bustled out, "your Uncle 'Lijer ain't been out here before this."

Adelaide laughed, and called to Big Jim, who was

stoking the stove with wood. "You go tell 'em we'll have supper after this dance," she said. "It's 'leven o'clock now and some of 'em'll want to be goin'. They can dance after."

Big Jim moved cumbersomely off. The house was hot and his store clothes irked.

Plates were taken down from the warming oven and filled. A slice of meat, thick and grayly pink, a spoonful of potatoes. The rolls, pickles, — peach and sweet cucumber, — and jelly would be passed.

The music ceased, and other women came out to help serve. Plates were taken in, and so were huge cups of coffee on huge saucers.

My mother began to cut the cakes: a custard cream cake which, as her knife clove the spongy loaf, oozed a thick luscious sauce. If not skillfully manipulated, this might prove disastrous to unbibbed fronts.

Besides this was a layer cake with raisin filling, and a chocolate cake reeking of fragrant sweet.

All this before our tortured eyes, with only an occasional furtively slipped tidbit from this or that to stay a clamoring appetite until the "company" had been taken care of and little girls could, as we were faithfully promised, be set up at the kitchen table and properly fed.

Into the midst of this there came to our surprised ears the tinkling whisper of sleighbells, approaching apparently from the barn. The sound neared, stopped at the kitchen door. To our shocked amazement my father's voice called lustily, " 'Miry!" And again, more loudly, " *'Mi*-ry!"

My mother went to the door. Adelaide, Cory, and I — and unnoted others — peered around her. There, bundled in overcoat, coonskin cap, scarf, and mittens, sat my father in the squat old pung, looking like a monstrous toad mounted on a snow-riding raft. The horse, apparently, had been cold. He tossed his head, pranced, jerked his tail.

"Whoa, there, you old fool coot!" admonished my father impatiently, and to my mother: "Hurry up, 'Miry. Old hoss wants to get home."

"'Lijer!" my mother's voice wailed at him. "We *can't* go now. We 're just goin' to eat!"

"You *can't* go now, Uncle 'Lijer," echoed Adelaide vociferously. "Who ever *heard* of such a thing? We 're just goin' to *eat!*"

"Why," my father turned a mildly astonished face upon them, " 'Miry *said* she did n't want to stay. And it 's 'leven o'clock now. Half the night 's gone. Whoa — there — you danged old fool. Better hurry up, 'Miry, it 's pretty cold."

The dismayed, astounded, disappointed faces withdrew. The door was slammed. Without a word, but with a face redder than contact with the blazing stove could make it, my mother took me by the hand and hurriedly drew me after her to the bedroom where our wraps were laid. Silently we put them on and made our way, among what seemed a wavering field of faces, back to the kitchen, where Adelaide met us with a generous-sized box securely tied.

"Here," she said, sympathetically, "I 've packed up some supper for you."

"No," said my mother firmly, "I 'm not going to take it. *That 's just what he 's figured on!*"

My father admonished the eager horse, and at the same time lent an anxious hand to our seating, pulled up the robes with unusual solicitude, and we were off with a bound of the old pung that all but landed us backward into the straw-lined box.

"*Now*," said my mother tightly after old Ned had been brought to his usual plodding pace, "I 'd like to know what you *mean!*"

"*Mean?*" repeated my father, spuriously surprised. "What d'*you* mean?"

"I mean I want to know what you sneaked out the front door for and hitched up without saying a word."

"I *did n't* sneak out the front door," replied my father, righteously affronted. "I went out the side door — "

"Yes, where nobody could see you!"

" 'T wa'n't nobody's business — "

"You *knew* supper was ready."

"Well, I did n't think you 'd want to stay to *supper*. Why, it 'd keep us there another *hour!* Midnight 'fore we'd get away. We stayed now longer 'n you wanted to."

My mother shrugged within her wraps. Shrugged, and said "Pffh!" but no more.

Finally, in a voice smooth as the field of starlit snow fading to gray beyond the limit of our sight, "Adelaide give you any of that supper to take home?" he asked. "Looked pretty good."

"Yes," snapped my mother, "she did. But I wouldn't take it. Why didn't you *stay* and *eat* it if you thought it looked so good?"

"I'll tell you!" His voice had lost its unctuous appeal. It sounded as it so often did — "tetchy." "If them women don't know any more 'n to expect a man to set there 'th a plate of vittles on his knees and a cup o' coffee in his hands, *all* the men ought to go home. How in *tunket* they expect to manage?"

Now he was the aggrieved, embarrassed, adolescent boy, afraid of being awkward or made ridiculous.

Actually, my mother laughed. Snickered a little in the fluffy folds of her nubia.

"Well," she said, "I knew you was proud as Lucifer, but it's the first time I ever knew your pride to get the best of your stomach. You got no supper and it serves you right."

In later years, when suffering myself from "refreshments," served either to sitting or to standing guests or by any misrepresentation of hospitality that does not include some kind of table board, I wondered if it did.

Just before we reached our own house my mother spoke again, apparently out of the reverie that had enveloped her.

"He's going to rue it," she stated in a tone of prophetic finality.

"Who?" My father's voice was thick with sleep.

"William, of course. He's made a mistake."

We drew up to the kitchen door. My father threw off the old buffalo robe and lumbered stiffly down from his seat. "Well," he said, "it's pretty late to think about it, ain't it?"

And so Adelaide's housewarming was over, and so was William's bride welcomed to her husband's home and into the lives — whether to the hearts or not — of his neighbors, friends, and kin. And so, to the haunting whims of Stib Obart's violin and the memorable swish of voluminous starched or silken skirts, with measured tap and beat of capering toe and heel, we fell asleep.

FOR THE COOK'S CONVENIENCE